Further Recollections

**Ten stories on five themes
Edited by
Mark Shackleton**

Longman Group Limited
Edinburgh Gate, Harlow,
Essex CM20 2JE, England
and Associated Companies throughout the world.

© Mark Shackleton 1989

First published by Edward Arnold, a division of Hodder and
Stoughton Ltd 1989. Reprinted once ISBN 0-340-50541-9

This edition published by Thomas Nelson and Sons Ltd 1991

This impression Longman Group Ltd. 1996

ISBN 0-17-556129-X

All rights reserved. No part of this publication may be
reproduced, copied or transmitted save with written permission
or in accordance with the provisions of the Copyright, Design
and Patents Act 1988, or under the terms of any licence
permitting limited copying issued by the Copyright Licensing
Agency, 90 Tottenham Court Road, London W1P 9HE.

Any person who does any unauthorised act in relation to this
publication may be liable to criminal prosecution and civil
claims for damages.

Printed in China
SWT/02

Introduction

Further Recollections is a collection of short stories covering five themes. All the stories are by well-known writers and should provide enjoyable reading to a higher intermediate or advanced student of English as a foreign or second language. The stories are unsimplified, so they are also suitable for the native speaker who may wish to read for study or pleasure.

Each theme is explored in two stories. This allows the reader to consider the treatment of an idea from two different viewpoints. Stan Barstow and Frank O'Connor, for example, provide contrasting studies of the problems of temptation and responsibility to a child, whilst Susan Hill and Katherine Mansfield offer two portraits of loneliness in middle age.

Question material on each story is intended to assist comprehension and appreciation. For this reason a more demanding main question is followed by a series of easier questions which, step by step, help the reader build up an understanding of the issues raised by the main question. The easier questions are primarily for the reader working alone; the main questions are possible starting points for group discussion. The glossaries give explanations *in context* and are intended to help the reader read fluently and with enjoyment. *Further Recollections* is a similar reader to *Recollections* (edited by Alex Adkins and Mark Shackleton, first published by Edward Arnold in 1980), with the exception of the addition of 'Language Activities' and 'Ideas for Writing', which are intended as a lively exploration of the text from both a linguistic and literary point of view.

It is recommended, but not absolutely essential, that the stories are read in the order in which they appear in the book. The reason for this is that some of the more difficult stories (e.g. those by James Thurber and Katherine Mansfield) appear towards the end of the book.

Abbreviations used in the glossaries

Am.E. : American English
Br.E. : British English
coll. : colloquial
dial. : dialect
idiom. : idiomatic
sl. : slang

Surprise

H.H. Munro (Saki) (1870–1916)

Hector Hugh Munro, who used the pen name 'Saki', was a master story writer. Born in Burma, the son of a Scottish official in the Burma police, he was brought to England at the age of two after his mother died. His early childhood was spent in the care of two very strict aunts. Later, after schooling in England, he and his father travelled throughout Europe. He worked as a journalist and published his first collection of short stories, *Reginald*, in 1904. He fought in the army from the beginning of the First World War and was killed in action in 1916.

Saki wrote three plays and three novels, but he is best known as a writer of humorous short stories. His wit is sharp, at times even cruel. All his works have been collected together in *The Complete Works of Saki* (1980).

The story

'Once upon a time,' began the bachelor, 'there was a little girl called Bertha, who was extraordinarily good . . . horribly good . . .' and suddenly his audience began to show an interest.

The Story-teller

IT WAS a hot afternoon, and the railway carriage was correspondingly sultry*, and the next stop was at Templecombe, nearly an hour ahead. The occupants of the carriage were a small girl, and a smaller girl, and a small boy. An aunt belonging to the children occupied one corner seat, and the farther corner seat on the opposite side was occupied by a bachelor who was a stranger to their party, but the small girls and the small boy emphatically occupied the compartment*. Both the aunt and the children were conversational in a limited, persistent* way, reminding one of the attentions of a housefly that refused to be discouraged. Most of the aunt's remarks seemed to begin with 'Don't', and nearly all of the children's remarks began with 'Why?' The bachelor said nothing out loud.

'Don't, Cyril, don't,' exclaimed the aunt, as the small boy began smacking the cushions of the seat, producing a cloud of dust at each blow.

'Come and look out of the window,' she added.

The child moved reluctantly to the window. 'Why are those sheep being driven out of that field?' he asked.

'I expect they are being driven to another field where there is more grass,' said the aunt weakly.

'But there is lots of grass in that field,' protested the boy; 'there's nothing else but grass there. Aunt, there's lots of grass in that field.'

'Perhaps the grass in the other field is better,' suggested the aunt fatuously*.

'Why is it better?' came the swift, inevitable* question.

'Oh, look at those cows!' exclaimed the aunt. Nearly every field along the line had contained cows or bullocks*, but she spoke as though she were drawing attention to a rarity.

'Why is the grass in the other field better?' persisted Cyril.

The frown* on the bachelor's face was deepening to a

scowl*. He was a hard, unsympathetic man, the aunt decided in her mind. She was utterly unable to come to any satisfactory decision about the grass in the other field.

The smaller girl created a diversion* by beginning to recite 'On the Road to Mandalay'*. She only knew the first line, but she put her limited knowledge to the fullest possible use. She repeated the line over and over again in a dreamy but resolute* and very audible voice; it seemed to the bachelor as though someone had had a bet with her that she could not repeat the line aloud two thousand times without stopping. Whoever it was who had made the wager was likely to lose his bet.

'Come over here and listen to a story,' said the aunt, when the bachelor had looked twice at her and once at the communication cord*.

The children moved listlessly* towards the aunt's end of the carriage. Evidently her reputation as a story-teller did not rank high* in their estimation.

In a low, confidential* voice, interrupted at frequent intervals by loud, petulant* questions from her listeners, she began an unenterprising* and deplorably uninteresting story about a little girl who was good, and made friends with everyone on account of her goodness, and was finally saved from a mad bull by a number of rescuers who admired her moral character.

'Wouldn't they have saved her if she hadn't been good?' demanded the bigger of the small girls. It was exactly the question that the bachelor had wanted to ask.

'Well, yes,' admitted the aunt lamely*, 'but I don't think they would have run quite so fast to her help if they had not liked her so much.'

'It's the stupidest story I've ever heard,' said the bigger of the small girls, with immense conviction*.

'I didn't listen after the first bit, it was so stupid,' said Cyril.

The smaller girl made no actual comment on the story, but she had long ago recommenced a murmured repetition of her favourite line.

'You don't seem to be a success as a story-teller,' said the bachelor suddenly from his corner.

The aunt bristled* in instant defence at this unexpected attack.

'It's a very difficult thing to tell stories that children can both understand and appreciate,' she said stiffly.

'I don't agree with you,' said the bachelor.

'Perhaps *you* would like to tell them a story,' was the aunt's retort*.

'Tell us a story,' demanded the bigger of the small girls.

'Once upon a time,' began the bachelor, 'there was a little girl called Bertha, who was extraordinarily good.'

The children's momentarily-aroused interest began at once to flicker*; all stories seemed dreadfully alike, no matter who told them.

'She did all that she was told, she was always truthful, she kept her clothes clean, ate milk puddings as though they were jam tarts, learned her lessons perfectly, and was polite in her manners.'

'Was she pretty?' asked the bigger of the small girls.

'Not as pretty as any of you,' said the bachelor, 'but she was horribly good.'

There was a wave of reaction in favour of this story; the word horrible in connection with goodness was a novelty that commended itself*. It seemed to introduce a ring* of truth that was absent from the aunt's tales of infant life.

'She was so good,' continued the bachelor, 'that she won several medals for goodness, which she always wore, pinned on to her dress. There was a medal for obedience*, another medal for punctuality*, and a third for good behaviour. They were large metal medals and they clinked against one another as she walked. No other child in the town where she lived had as many as three medals, so everybody knew that she must be an extra good child.'

'Horribly good,' quoted Cyril.

'Everybody talked about her goodness, and the Prince of the country got to hear about it, and he said that as she was so very good she might be allowed once a week to walk in his park, which was just outside the town. It was a beautiful park, and no children were ever allowed in it, so it was a great honour for Bertha to be allowed to go there.'

'Were there any sheep in the park?' demanded Cyril.

'No,' said the bachelor, 'there were no sheep.'

'Why weren't there any sheep?' came the inevitable question arising out of that answer.

The aunt permitted herself a smile, which might almost have been described as a grin*.

'There were no sheep in the park,' said the bachelor, 'because the Prince's mother had once had a dream that her son would either be killed by a sheep or else by a clock falling on him. For that reason the Prince never kept a sheep in his park or a clock in his palace.'

The aunt suppressed* a gasp* of admiration.

'Was the Prince killed by a sheep or by a clock?' asked Cyril.

'He is still alive, so we can't tell whether the dream will come true,' said the bachelor unconcernedly; 'anyway, there were no sheep in the park, but there were lots of little pigs running all over the place.'

'What colour were they?'

'Black with white faces, white with black spots, black all over, grey with white patches, and some were white all over.'

The story-teller paused to let a full idea of the park's treasures sink into the children's imaginations; then he resumed*:

'Bertha was rather sorry to find that there were no flowers in the park. She had promised her aunts, with tears in her eyes, that she would not pick any of the kind Prince's flowers, and she had meant to keep her promise, so of course it made her feel silly to find that there were no flowers to pick.'

'Why weren't there any flowers?'

'Because the pigs had eaten them all,' said the bachelor promptly*. 'The gardeners had told the Prince that you couldn't have pigs and flowers, so he decided to have pigs and no flowers.'

There was a murmur* of approval at the excellence of the Prince's decision; so many people would have decided the other way.

'There were lots of other delightful things in the park. There were ponds with gold and blue and green fish in them, and trees with beautiful parrots that said clever things at a moment's notice*, and humming birds* that hummed all the popular tunes of the day. Bertha walked up and down and enjoyed herself immensely, and thought to herself: ''If I were not so extraordinarily good I should not have been allowed to come into this beautiful park and enjoy all that there is to be seen in it,'' and her three medals clinked against one another as she walked and helped to remind her how very good she really was. Just then an enormous wolf came prowling* into the park to see if it could catch a fat little pig for its supper.'

'What colour was it?' asked the children, amid an immediate quickening of interest.

'Mud-colour all over, with a black tongue and pale grey eyes that gleamed with unspeakable ferocity*. The first thing that it saw in the park was Bertha; her pinafore* was so spotlessly white and clean that it could be seen from a great distance. Bertha saw the wolf and saw that it was stealing towards her, and she began to wish that she had never been allowed to come into the park. She ran as hard as she could, and the wolf came after her with huge leaps and bounds*. She managed to reach a shrubbery* of myrtle* bushes and she hid herself in one of the thickest of the bushes. The wolf came sniffing among the branches, its black tongue lolling* out of its mouth and its pale grey eyes glaring with rage. Bertha was terribly frightened, and thought to herself: ''If I had not been so extraordinarily good I should have been safe in the town at this moment.'' However, the scent of the myrtle was so strong that the wolf could not sniff out where Bertha was hiding, and the bushes were so thick that he might have hunted about in them for a long time without catching sight of her, so he thought he might as well go off and catch a little pig instead. Bertha was trembling very much at having the wolf prowling and sniffing so near her, and as she trembled the medal for obedience clinked against the medals for good conduct and punctuality. The wolf was just moving away when he heard the sound of the medals clinking and stopped to listen; they clinked again in a bush quite near him. He dashed into the bush, his pale grey eyes gleaming with ferocity and triumph, and dragged Bertha out and devoured* her to the last morsel*. All that was left of her were her shoes, bits of clothing, and the three medals for goodness.'

'Were any of the little pigs killed?'

'No, they all escaped.'

'The story began badly,' said the smaller of the small girls, 'but it had a beautiful ending.'

'It is the most beautiful story that I ever heard,' said the bigger of the small girls, with immense decision.

'It is the only beautiful story I have ever heard,' said Cyril.

A dissentient* opinion came from the aunt.

'A most improper story to tell to young children! You have undermined* the effect of years of careful teaching.'

'At any rate,' said the bachelor, collecting his belongings preparatory to* leaving the carriage, 'I kept them quiet for ten minutes, which was more than you were able to do.'

'Unhappy woman!' he observed to himself as he walked down the platform of Templecombe station; 'for the next six months or so those children will assail* her in public with demands for an improper story!'

Glossary

The meanings given below are those which the words and phrases have as they occur in the story.

Page

3   *sultry*: hot and airless.

    compartment: separate division in a railway carriage.

    persistent: carrying on without giving up.

    fatuously: foolishly.

    inevitable: certain to happen.

    bullocks: young bulls which cannot breed.

    frown: serious and displeased look.

4   *scowl*: angry, bad-tempered look.

    diversion: something that turns the attention to something else.

    'On the Road to Mandalay': a well-known poem by the English writer, Rudyard Kipling (1865–1936).

    resolute: fixed in purpose.

    communication cord: chain that can be pulled to stop the train in an emergency.

    listlessly: without energy or interest.

    rank high: have a high place.

    confidential: spoken as though telling a secret.

    petulant: impatient and bad-tempered.

    unenterprising: unimaginative.

    lamely: weakly.

    immense conviction: a very strong belief in what she says.

5   *bristled*: became angry.

    retort: quick rather angry reply.

    flicker: become less strong.

    commended itself: was worth taking an interest in.

    ring: sense.

    obedience: doing what one is told to do.

    punctuality: arriving at the proper time (to school, meals etc.).

6   *grin*: a wide smile that shows the teeth.

    suppressed: controlled.

    gasp: short, surprised taking in of breath.

resumed: began the story again.
promptly: at once.
murmur: low sound.

7   *a moment's notice*: suddenly.
humming birds: very small birds that make a humming (singing with closed lips) sound with their wings when they fly.
prowling: moving silently and secretly.
ferocity: fierceness.
pinafore: loose garment worn over a dress to keep it clean.
with huge leaps and bounds: moving very quickly.
shrubbery: group of bushes.
myrtle: a bush with sweet-smelling white flowers.
lolling: hanging down.
devoured: ate quickly and hungrily.

8   *morsel*: very small piece.
dissentient: strongly disagreeing.
undermined: destroyed.
preparatory to: before.
assail: keep annoying.

Questions

1. What kind of person is the aunt?

   (a) In what way is the aunt's handling of the children negative? (p. 3)
   (b) Why is she unsuccessful in interesting the children in what is going on outside the train window? (p. 3)
   (c) We are given the aunt's reactions whilst the bachelor is telling his story. (p. 6) What do they tell us about the kind of person the aunt is?
   (d) Judging from her story (p. 4) and her reactions after the bachelor has finished his (p. 8), what does the aunt think the purpose of a story should be?

2. What are the children like?

   (a) Cyril smacks the cushions (p. 3) and the smaller girl

repeats one line of poetry over and over again. (p. 4)
Why?

(b) Where and why do the children first become interested
in the bachelor's story? (p. 5)

(c) What aspects of the bachelor's story are the children
particularly interested in? (pp. 6–8) What does that tell
us about them?

(d) After both the aunt and the bachelor have finished their
stories the children give their opinions. (p. 4, p. 8)
What do they tell us about the children?

3. In what ways is the bachelor's story similar to traditional
fairy tales?

(a) Are the opening words of the bachelor's story a typical
fairy tale beginning? (p. 5)

(b) Consider the animals and the people in the bachelor's
story. (pp. 6–7) Which of them would you say are often
found in fairy tales and which are not?

(c) Are there any similarities between such tales as *Little
Red Riding Hood* and *The Wolf and the Three Little
Pigs* and the bachelor's story?

4. What are the surprising aspects of the bachelor's story?

(a) Where is the first sign that the bachelor's story will be
different from a typical children's story? (p. 5)

(b) The bachelor explains why there are no sheep in the
park. What is surprising about his explanation? (p. 6)

(c) How does the bachelor make fun of Bertha in the paragraph beginning 'Bertha was rather sorry to find that
there were no flowers in the park.'? (p. 6)

(d) In what ways is Bertha punished for her goodness?
(p. 7)

Language Activities

Differences in Meaning

Explain the differences in meaning between the following passages from the text (a) and an altered version of the text (b).

1. (a) . . . *the bachelor had looked twice at her and once at the communication cord.* (p. 4)
   (b) . . . *the bachelor had looked twice at her* and the rest of the time he looked angry.

2. (a) . . . *she was horribly good.* (p. 5)
   (b) . . . *she was* very good.

3. (a) *The story-teller paused to let a full idea of the park's treasures sink into the children's imaginations* . . . (p. 6)
   (b) *The story-teller paused to let a full idea of the park's* animals *sink into the children's imaginations* . . .

4. (a) *She had promised her aunts, with tears in her eyes, that she would not pick any of the kind Prince's flowers* . . . (p. 6)
   (b) *She had promised her aunts that she would not pick any of the kind Prince's flowers* . . .

5. (a) . . . *she had meant to keep her promise, so of course it made her feel silly to find there were no flowers to pick.* (p. 6)
   (b) . . . *she had meant to keep her promise,* so she was glad *to find there were no flowers to pick.*

6. (a) *There were . . . humming birds that hummed all the popular tunes of the day.* (p. 7)
   (b) *There were . . . humming birds that* made a humming sound with their wings.

7. (a) '*If I were not so extraordinarily good I should not have been allowed to come into this beautiful park . . .*' (p. 7)

   (b) '*If I were not a good girl I should not have been allowed to come into this beautiful park . . .*'

8. (a)   *. . . and as she trembled the medal for obedience clinked against the medals for good conduct and punctuality.* (p. 7)

   (b)   *. . . and as she trembled the* three medals clinked together.

Ideas for Writing

1. Write your own children's story beginning 'Once upon a time there was a little _____ called _____, who was extraordinarily _____, in fact she was horribly _____ . . . ' Fill in the gaps with words of your choice.

2. The aunt tells a story about a good little girl and a mad bull. Write out the story as the bachelor might tell it. Begin 'Once upon a time . . .'

3. Write out a children's story or fairy tale that you know well, changing it in any way you like.

W. Somerset Maugham (1874–1965)

William Somerset Maugham is one of the most popular English authors of the twentieth century. He wrote plays, novels and short stories, some of which have been televised and filmed. During his long and interesting life Maugham worked for the British secret service in both World Wars and also travelled widely. His stories, too, are placed in varied settings, including the Far East and Europe, and are about a wide variety of characters. His stories are witty and sophisticated, and he is a master of the well-written story line, which frequently concludes with a surprise ending. His *Complete Short Stories* are collected in three volumes, and his best-known novels are *Of Human Bondage* (1915), *Cakes and Ale* (1930) and *The Razor's Edge* (1944).

The story

Albert Edward Foreman had performed his duties as verger (church caretaker) of St Peter's, Neville Square, London, for sixteen years. Nobody had any complaints to make about the verger, that is, not until the new vicar arrived.

The Verger*

T HERE had been a christening that afternoon at St
Peter's, Neville Square, and Albert Edward Foreman still
wore his verger's gown. He kept his new one, its folds as full
and stiff as though it were made not of alpaca* but of perennial* bronze, for funerals and weddings (St Peter's, Neville
Square, was a church much favoured by the fashionable for
these ceremonies) and now he wore only his second-best. He
wore it with complacence*, for it was the dignified symbol of
his office, and without it (when he took it off to go home) he
had the disconcerting* sensation of being somewhat insufficiently clad*. He took pains with it; he pressed it and ironed it
himself. During the sixteen years he had been verger of this
church he had had a succession of such gowns, but he had
never been able to throw them away when they were worn out
and the complete series, neatly wrapped up in brown paper,
lay in the bottom drawers of the wardrobe in his bedroom.

The verger busied himself quietly, replacing the painted
wooden cover on the marble font*, taking away a chair that
had been brought for an infirm old lady, and waited for the
vicar to have finished in the vestry* so that he could tidy up
in there and go home. Presently he saw him walk across the
chancel*, genuflect* in front of the high altar, and come down
the aisle; but he still wore his cassock*.

'What's he 'anging about for?' the verger said to himself.
'Don't 'e know I want my tea?'

The vicar had been but recently appointed, a red-faced energetic man in the early forties, and Albert Edward still regretted
his predecessor, a clergyman of the old school* who preached
leisurely sermons in a silvery voice and dined out a great deal
with his more aristocratic parishioners*. He liked things in
church to be just so, but he never fussed; he was not like this
new man who wanted to have his finger in every pie. But
Albert Edward was tolerant. St Peter's was in a very good
neighbourhood and the parishioners were a very nice class of

people. The new vicar had come from the East End* and he couldn't be expected to fall in all at once with the discreet ways of his fashionable congregation.*

'All this 'ustle*,' said Albert Edward. 'But give 'im time, he'll learn.'

When the vicar had walked down the aisle so far that he could address the verger without raising his voice more than was becoming in a place of worship he stopped.

'Foreman, will you come into the vestry for a minute. I have something to say to you.'

'Very good, sir.'

The vicar waited for him to come up and they walked up the church together.

'A very nice christening, I thought, sir. Funny 'ow the baby stopped cryin' the moment you took him.'

'I've noticed they very often do,' said the vicar, with a little smile. 'After all I've had a good deal of practice with them.'

It was a source of subdued* pride to him that he could nearly always quiet a whimpering infant by the manner in which he held it and he was not unconscious of the amused admiration with which mothers and nurses watched him settle the baby in the crook of his surpliced* arm. The verger knew that it pleased him to be complimented on his talent.

The vicar preceded Albert Edward into the vestry. Albert Edward was a trifle* surprised to find the two churchwardens* there. He had not seen them come in. They gave him pleasant nods.

'Good afternoon, my lord. Good afternoon, sir,' he said to one after the other.

They were elderly men, both of them, and they had been churchwardens almost as long as Albert Edward had been verger. They were sitting now at a handsome refectory* table that the old vicar had brought many years before from Italy and the vicar sat down in the vacant chair between them. Albert Edward faced them, the table between him and them, and wondered with slight uneasiness what was the matter. He remembered still the occasion on which the organist had got into trouble and the bother they had all had to hush things up.

In a church like St Peter's, Neville Square, they couldn't afford a scandal. On the vicar's red face was a look of resolute benignity*, but the others bore an expression that was slightly troubled.

'He's been naggin' them, he 'as,' said the verger to himself. 'He's jockeyed them into doin' something, but they don't 'alf like it. That's what it is, you mark my words.'

But his thoughts did not appear on Albert Edward's clean-cut and distinguished features. He stood in a respectful but not obsequious* attitude. He had been in service* before he was appointed to his ecclesiastical office, but only in very good houses, and his deportment* was irreproachable*. Starting as a page-boy* in the household of a merchant-prince, he had risen by due degrees from the position of fourth to first footman*, for a year he had been single-handed butler* to a widowed peeress*, and, till the vacancy occurred at St Peter's, butler with two men under him in the house of a retired ambassador. He was tall, spare*, grave*, and dignified. He looked, if not like a duke, at least like an actor of the old school who specialized in duke's parts. He had tact, firmness, and self-assurance. His character was unimpeachable*.

The vicar began briskly*.

'Foreman, we've got something rather unpleasant to say to you. You've been here a great many years and I think his lordship and the general agree with me that you've fulfilled the duties of your office to the satisfaction of everybody concerned.'

The two churchwardens nodded.

'But a most extraordinary circumstance came to my knowledge the other day and I felt it my duty to impart it to the churchwardens. I discovered to my astonishment that you could neither read nor write.'

The verger's face betrayed no sign of embarrassment.

'The last vicar knew that, sir,' he replied. 'He said it didn't make no difference. He always said there was a great deal too much education in the world for 'is taste.'

'It's the most amazing thing I ever heard,' cried the general. 'Do you mean to say that you've been verger of this church for sixteen years and never learned to read or write?'

'I went into service when I was twelve, sir. The cook in the first place tried to teach me once, but I didn't seem to 'ave the knack* for it, and then what with one thing and another I never seemed to 'ave the time. I've never really found the want of it. I think a lot of these young fellows waste a rare* lot of time readin' when they might be doin' something useful.'

'But don't you want to know the news?' said the other churchwarden. 'Don't you ever want to write a letter?'

'No, me lord, I seem to manage very well without. And of late years now they've all these pictures in the papers I get to know what's goin' on pretty well. Me wife's quite a scholar and if I want to write a letter she writes it for me. It's not as if I was a bettin' man.'

The two churchwardens gave the vicar a troubled glance and then looked down at the table.

'Well, Foreman, I've talked the matter over with these gentlemen and they quite agree with me that the situation is impossible. At a church like St Peter's, Neville Square, we cannot have a verger who can neither read nor write.'

Albert Edward's thin, sallow* face reddened and he moved uneasily on his feet, but he made no reply.

'Understand me, Foreman, I have no complaint to make against you. You do your work quite satisfactorily; I have the highest opinion both of your character and of your capacity; but we haven't the right to take the risk of some accident that might happen owing to your lamentable* ignorance. It's a matter of prudence* as well as of principle.'

'But couldn't you learn, Foreman?' asked the general.

'No, sir, I'm afraid I couldn't, not now. You see, I'm not as young as I was and if I couldn't seem able to get the letters in me 'ead when I was a nipper* I don't think there's much chance of it now.'

'We don't want to be harsh* with you, Foreman,' said the vicar. 'But the churchwardens and I have quite made up our minds. We'll give you three months and if at the end of that time you cannot read and write I'm afraid you'll have to go.'

Albert Edward had never liked the new vicar. He'd said

from the beginning that they'd made a mistake when they gave him St Peter's. He wasn't the type of man they wanted with a classy congregation like that. And now he straightened himself a little. He knew his value and he wasn't going to allow himself to be put upon.

'I'm very sorry, sir, I'm afraid it's no good. I'm too old a dog to learn new tricks. I've lived a good many years without knowin' 'ow to read and write, and without wishin' to praise myself, self-praise is no recommendation, I don't mind sayin' I've done my duty in that state of life in which it 'as pleased a merciful providence* to place me, and if I could learn now I don't know as I'd want to.'

'In that case, Foreman, I'm afraid you must go.'

'Yes, sir, I quite understand. I shall be 'appy to 'and in my resignation as soon as you've found somebody to take my place.'

But when Albert Edward with his usual politeness had closed the church door behind the vicar and the two church-wardens he could not sustain the air of unruffled* dignity with which he had borne the blow inflicted upon him and his lips quivered*. He walked slowly back to the vestry and hung up on its proper peg his verger's gown. He sighed as he thought of all the grand funerals and smart weddings it had seen. He tidied everything up, put on his coat, and hat in hand walked down the aisle. He locked the church door behind him. He strolled across the square, but deep in his sad thoughts he did not take the street that led him home, where a nice strong cup of tea awaited him; he took the wrong turning. He walked slowly along. His heart was heavy. He did not know what he should do with himself. He did not fancy the notion of going back to domestic service; after being his own master for so many years, for the vicar and churchwardens could say what they liked, it was he that had run St Peter's, Neville Square, he could scarcely demean* himself by accepting a situation. He had saved a tidy sum, but not enough to live on without doing something, and life seemed to cost more every year. He had never thought to be troubled with such questions. The vergers of St Peter's, like the popes of Rome, were there for life. He had often thought of the pleasant reference the vicar would make in his sermon at evensong* the first Sunday after his death to the long and faithful service, and the exemplary* character of their late* verger, Albert Edward Foreman. He sighed deeply. Albert Edward was a non-smoker and a total abstainer*, but with a certain latitude*; that is to say he liked a glass of beer with his dinner and when he was tired he enjoyed a cigarette. It occurred to him now that one would comfort him and since he did not carry them he looked about him for a shop where he could buy a packet of Gold Flakes*. He did not at once see one and walked on a little. It was a long street, with all sorts of shops in it, but there was not a single one where you could buy cigarettes.

'That's strange,' said Albert Edward.

To make sure he walked right up the street again. No, there was no doubt about it. He stopped and looked reflectively up and down.

'I can't be the only man as walks along this street and wants a fag*,' he said. 'I shouldn't wonder but what a fellow might do very well with a little shop here. Tobacco and sweets, you know.'

He gave a sudden start*.

'That's an idea,' he said. 'Strange 'ow things come to you when you least expect it.'

He turned, walked home, and had his tea.

'You're very silent this afternoon, Albert,' his wife remarked.

'I'm thinkin',' he said.

He considered the matter from every point of view and next day he went along the street and by good luck found a little shop to let* that looked as though it would exactly suit him. Twenty-four hours later he had taken it, and when a month after that he left St Peter's, Neville Square, for ever, Albert Edward Foreman set up in business as a tobacconist and news-agent. His wife said it was a dreadful come-down* after being verger of St Peter's, but he answered that you had to move with the times, the church wasn't what it was, and 'ence forward he was going to render unto Caesar what was Caesar's*.

Albert Edward did very well. He did so well that in a year or so it struck him that he might take a second shop and put a manager in. He looked for another long street that hadn't got a tobacconist in it and when he found it, and a shop to let, took it and stocked* it. This was a success too. Then it occurred to him that if he could run two he could run half a dozen, so he began walking about London, and whenever he found a long street that had no tobacconist and a shop to let he took it. In the course of ten years he had acquired no less than ten shops and he was making money hand over fist*. He went round to all of them himself every Monday, collected the week's takings, and took them to the bank.

One morning when he was there paying in a bundle of notes and a heavy bag of silver the cashier told him that the manager would like to see him. He was shown into an office and the manager shook hands with him.

'Mr Foreman, I wanted to have a talk to you about the money you've got on deposit* with us. D'you know exactly how much it is?'

'Not within a pound or two, sir; but I've got a pretty rough idea.'

'Apart from what you paid in this morning it's a little over thirty thousand pounds. That's a very large sum to have on deposit and I should have thought you'd do better to invest it.'

'I wouldn't want to take no risk, sir. I know's it's safe in the bank.'

'You needn't have the least anxiety. We'll make you out a list of absolutely gilt-edged securities*. They'll bring you in a better rate of interest* than we can possibly afford to give you.'

A troubled look settled on Mr Foreman's distinguished face. 'I've never 'ad anything to do with stocks and shares* and I'd 'ave to leave it all in your 'ands,' he said.

The manager smiled. 'We'll do everything. All you'll have to do next time you come in is just to sign the transfers*.'

'I could do that all right,' said Albert uncertainly. 'But 'ow should I know what I was signin'?'

'I suppose you can read,' said the manager a trifle sharply.

Mr Foreman gave him a disarming* smile.

'Well, sir, that's just it. I can't. I know it sounds funny-like, but there it is, I can't read or write, only me name, an' I only learnt to do that when I went into business.'

The manager was so surprised that he jumped up from his chair.

'That's the most extraordinary thing I ever heard.'

'You see, it's like this, sir, I never 'ad the opportunity until it was too late and then some'ow I wouldn't. I got obstinate-like.'

The manager stared at him as though he were a prehistoric monster.

'And do you mean to say that you've built up this important business and amassed a fortune of thirty thousand pounds without being able to read or write? Good God, man, what would you be now if you had been able to?'

'I can tell you that, sir,' said Mr Foreman, a little smile on his still aristocratic features. 'I'd be verger of St Peter's, Neville Square.'

Glossary

The meanings given below are those which the words and phrases have as they occur in the story.

Note: Albert Foreman has a rather uneducated way of speaking shown by the way he drops the 'h's' from the beginning of words and the 'g's' from their ends.

Page

15 *Verger*: an official in a church with various duties, for example to show people to their seats and to look after the church.

alpaca: a type of wool.

perennial: lasting for a very long time.

complacence: self-satisfaction.

disconcerting: worrying.

insufficiently clad: without enough clothing.

font: a large basin where holy water is kept for baptism.

vestry: room in a church where the vicar's and choir's special clothes are kept.

chancel: the eastern part of a church where the priest and choir usually sit.

genuflect: bend his knee as a sign of religious respect.

cassock: long (usually) black garment worn by a priest.

the old school: the old traditions.

parishioners: people who live in the church district.

16 *the East End*: the eastern part of London, then an area of poorer people.

congregation: group of people worshipping in a church together.

'ustle: (hustle) hurry.

subdued: hidden, submerged.

surpliced: a surplice is a white loose-fitting garment worn by a vicar.

a trifle: a little.

churchwardens: elected representatives who help manage the church's money and business matters.

refectory: dining-hall (for monks and priests).

17 *resolute benignity*: a look of determined kindness.

obsequious: too humble.
in service: employed as a servant.
deportment: way of standing and walking.
irreproachable: faultless.
page-boy: boy servant.
footman: manservant who opens the front door, waits at table etc.
butler: head manservant.
peeress: wife of a nobleman.
spare: thin.
grave: serious.
unimpeachable: impossible to find fault with.
briskly: quickly.

18 *knack*: ability.
rare: great.
sallow: yellowish.
lamentable: shameful.
prudence: wisdom.
nipper (Br.E. coll.): small boy.
harsh: unkind.

19 *merciful providence*: kind fate.
unruffled: calm.
quivered: trembled.
demean: lower.

20 *evensong*: evening service in the Church of England.
exemplary:a model, an example for others.
late: recently dead.
abstainer: person who does not drink alcohol.
latitude: freedom.
Gold Flakes: a brand of English cigarette.
fag (Br.E. sl.): cigarette.
start: quick movement of surprise.
to let: offered for renting.
come-down: fall in social position.
render unto Caesar . . . Caesar's: do what has to be done.

21 *stocked*: filled it with things he would sell.
hand over fist: very quickly.
on deposit: in a bank account.

gilt-edged securities: safe investments.

rate of interest: the money paid back to you after you have invested your money.

stocks and shares: types of investments.

transfers: papers giving permission for the money to be invested.

22 *disarming*: making it difficult for the bank manager to feel angry.

Questions

1. What information are we given that tells us that Albert Foreman is very suitable for his job as a verger at St Peter's, Neville Square?

    (a) List in order the jobs that Albert Foreman has had. (p. 17)

    (b) What sort of people has he worked for? (p. 17) In what ways are they similar to the congregation of St Peter's? (pp. 15–16)

    (c) What does Albert Foreman look like and what is his character like? (p. 17)

    (d) In the first paragraph we are told that St Peter's is a popular church for certain events. What events? (p. 15) When Albert resigns what especially does he remember about his work as verger? (p. 19)

2. In what ways is Albert Foreman's dignity emphasized in the story?

    (a) In what ways does Albert take good care of his verger's gowns? (p. 15) Why does he take such good care of them? (p. 15)

    (b) Why does Albert prefer to lose his job rather than learn how to read and write? (p. 19)

    (c) Why does Albert not wish to become a servant again after losing his job as verger? (p. 19)

    (d) What words given in the last few lines of the story show that Albert still looks dignified ten years after leaving St Peter's? (p. 22)

3. What differences are there between the present and the former vicar of St Peter's?

   (a) Look at the paragraph beginning 'The vicar had but recently been appointed . . .' (p. 15) How is the present vicar's way of doing his job different from the former vicar's?

   (b) In what way is the congregation of St Peter's different from the sort of congregation the present vicar is used to? (pp. 15–16) What detail shows the kind of relationship the former vicar had with his parishioners? (p. 15)

   (c) How did the two vicars react to the fact that Albert Foreman could not read or write? (p. 17)

4. What different sorts of surprises are there in the story?

   (a) What is the first surprise in the story, which the vicar finds 'extraordinary' and the general 'amazing'? (p. 17)

   (b) Albert's face reddens and he moves uneasily on his feet. What is his surprise? (p. 18)

   (c) Albert gives a sudden start in the street. What surprise is this? (p. 20)

   (d) The bank manager finds out that Albert cannot read or write. What does he do that shows he is surprised? (p. 22) What does he say? (p. 22) Who has said something similar earlier in the story? (p. 17)

   (e) Albert's final words (p. 22) are a surprise. To whom?

Language Activities

Literary and Non-literary Character Description

Imagine that you saw someone robbing a bank and went to report the crime to the police. The description you would give of the robber would concentrate on his **physical appearance**. You might say something like this:

He was a *tall* man, with *dark hair* and a *large nose* . . .

If, however, you were asked to give a reference for someone who was applying for a job you would concentrate on the person's **character**, not his or her physical appearance. You might write:

I have known John Smith for three years and have always found him a *highly intelligent* and *hard-working* employee.

You would not, of course, write that he was a '*tall, highly intelligent* and *hard-working* employee.'

However, in literary texts, **physical appearance** often tells the reader something about a person's **character**. Take this description from 'The Verger', for example:

The vicar . . ., a *red-faced energetic* man in the early forties . . . (p. 15)

Red-faced is his physical appearance, *energetic* is his character. The combined impression suggests someone who has a red face because he is always energetic, perhaps too energetic, for we soon find out he is *fussy*. When we later read:

On the vicar's red face was a look of resolute benignity (p. 17)

the image of his red face (a **physical** detail) will probably remind us of his energy and his fussiness (i.e. his **character**). Below is the fullest character description of Albert Foreman given in the story:

He was tall, spare, grave, and dignified. He looked, if not like a duke, at least like an actor of the old school who specialized in duke's parts. He had tact, firmness, and self-assurance. His character was unimpeachable. (p. 17)

a) Draw up a list of words from the above extract that describe Albert's physical appearance and another list of words that give his character.

b) Draw up a list of words that could be used to describe a person's height and build. Could any of them be used to describe Albert Foreman? Say why some would be appropriate and others would be inappropriate.

Ideas for Writing

1. Imagine that Albert Foreman has suddenly gone missing and Mrs Foreman goes to the police station to give a description of what he looks like. Write out what she says. Begin 'I want to report that my husband's gone missing. He's sixty years old . . .'

2. Imagine that Albert Foreman needs a character reference for a new job. You are either the former vicar or the present vicar. Write out a reference for Albert Foreman. Begin 'To Whom It May Concern. I have known Mr Albert Foreman for 16 years/eight months and . . .'.

3. After a long and successful life Albert Foreman dies. Imagine you are a journalist for a local newspaper. Write a short article on Albert's life. Begin: 'Albert Foreman died peacefully last week at the age of 87 after a long and successful life. He began humbly as a page-boy . . .'

* * * * * *

1. Which of these two stories do you prefer? What are some of the reasons for your choice?

2. Are the surprises equally unexpected in both stories?

3. What attitudes or types of people are being criticized in the two stories? Are both stories using humour to make their criticisms?

Temptation

Stan Barstow

Stan Barstow was born in Yorkshire, a heavily industrialized part of northern England, in 1928. The only son of a coal miner, he worked in industrial engineering until 1962. It was the success of his first novel, *A Kind of Loving* (1960), later filmed, that allowed him to become a full-time writer. His best-known novels are *Ask Me Tomorrow*, *Joby*, *The Watchers on the Shore* and *A Raging Calm*, and he has also written two collections of short stories, *Season with Eros* and *The Desperadoes* (1961), from which 'One of the Virtues' is taken. This story, as well as much of his other work, is set in a typical industrial town in Yorkshire, which Barstow calls Cressley.

Apart from novels and short stories, Stan Barstow has also written for radio, television and theatre.

The story

Will is ten. His grandfather, now dying, has worked as a blacksmith for five times Will's age. If only Will can inherit his grandfather's patience, then his future looks good. On the other hand, he may follow in the footsteps of his impatient father . . .

One of the Virtues

T HE watch belonged to my grandfather and it hung on a hook by the head of his bed where he had lain for many long weeks. The face was marked off in Roman numerals, the most elegant figures I had ever seen. The case was of gold, heavy and beautifully chased*; and the chain was of gold too, and wonderfully rich and smooth in the hand. The mechanism, when you held the watch to your ear, gave such a deep, steady ticking that you could not imagine its ever going wrong. It was altogether a most magnificent watch and when I sat with my grandfather in the late afternoon, after school, I could not keep my eyes away from it, dreaming that someday I too might own such a watch.

It was almost a ritual for me to sit with my grandfather for a little while after tea. My mother said he was old and drawing near his time*, and it seemed to me that he must be an incredible age. He liked me to read to him from the evening paper while he lay there, his long hands, soft and white now from disuse and fined down to skin and bone by illness and age, fluttered restlessly about over the sheets, like a blind man reading braille*. He had never been much of a reader himself and it was too much of an effort for him now. Possibly because he had had so little education, no one believed in it more, and he was always eager for news of my progress at school. The day I brought home the news of my success in the County Minor Scholarship examination he sent out for half an ounce of twist* and found the strength to sit up in bed for a smoke.

'Grammar School* next, then, Will?'· he said, pleased as Punch*.

'Then college,' I said, seeing the path straight before me. 'Then I shall be a doctor.'

'Aye, that he will*, I've no doubt,' my grandfather said. 'But he'll need plenty o' patience afore that day. Patience an' hard work, Will lad.'

Though, as I have said, he had little book-learning, I thought sometimes as I sat with my grandfather that he must be one of the wisest men in Yorkshire*; and these two qualities – patience and the ability to work hard – were the corner-stones* of his philosophy of life.

'Yes, Grandad,' I told him. 'I can wait.'

'Aye, Will, that's t'way* to do it. That's t'way to get on, lad.'

The smoke was irritating his throat and he laid aside the pipe with a sigh that seemed to me to contain regret for all the bygone pleasures of a lifetime and he fidgeted* with the sheets. 'It must be gettin' on*, Will . . .'

I took down the watch and gave it to him. He gazed at it for some moments, winding it up a few turns. When he passed it back to me I held it, feeling the weight of it.

'I reckon he'll be after a watch like that hisself*, one day, eh, Will?'

I smiled shyly, for I had not meant to covet* the watch so openly. 'Someday, Grandad,' I said. I could never really imagine the day such a watch could be mine.

'That watch wa' gi'n* me for fifty year o' service wi' my firm,' my grandfather said. ' "A token of appreciation," they said . . . It's theer*, in t'back, for you to see . . .'

I opened the back and looked at the inscription there: 'For loyal service . . .'

Fifty years . . . My grandfather had been a blacksmith*. It was hard now to believe that these pale, almost transparent hands had held the giant tongs* or directed the hammer in its mighty downward swing. Fifty years . . . Five times my own age. And the watch, prize of hard work and loyalty, hung, proudly cherished, at the head of the bed in which he was resting out his days. I think my grandfather spoke to me as he did partly because of the great difference in our ages and partly because of my father. My mother never spoke of my father and it was my grandfather who cut away some of the mystery with which my mother's silence had shrouded* him. My father, Grandfather told me, had been a promising young man cursed with a weakness. Impatience was his weakness: he was impatient to make money, to be a success, to impress his friends; and he lacked the perseverance* to approach success steadily. One after the other he abandoned his projects, and he and my mother were often unsure of their next meal. Then at last, while I was still learning to walk, my father, reviling* the lack of opportunity in the mother country, set off for the other side of the world and was never heard of again. All this my grandfather told me, not with bitterness or anger, for I gathered he had liked my father, but with sorrow that a good man should have gone astray* for want of what, to my grandfather, was a simple virtue, and brought such a hard life to my mother, Grandfather's daughter.

So my grandfather drifted to the end; and remembering those restless fingers I believe he came as near to losing his patience then as at any time in his long life.

One evening at the height of summer, as I prepared to leave him for the night, he put out his hand and touched mine. 'Thank y', lad,' he said in a voice grown very tired and weak. 'An' he'll not forget what I've told him?'

I was suddenly very moved; a lump came into my throat. 'No, Grandad,' I told him, 'I'll not forget.'

He gently patted my hand, then looked away and closed his eyes. The next morning my mother told me that he had died in his sleep.

They laid him out* in the damp mustiness* of his own front room, among the tasselled chairback covers and the lustres under their thin glass domes; and they let me see him for a moment. I did not stay long with him. He looked little different from the scores* of times I had seen him during his illness, except that his fretting* hands were stilled beneath the sheet and his hair and moustache had the inhuman antiseptic cleanliness of death. Afterwards, in the quiet of my own room, I cried a little, remembering that I should see him no more, and that I had talked with him and read to him for the last time.

After the funeral the family descended upon us in force* for the reading of the will. There was not much to quarrel about: my grandfather had never made much money, and what little he left had been saved slowly, thriftily over the years. It was divided fairly evenly along with the value of the house, the only condition being that the house was not to be sold, but that my mother was to be allowed to live in it and take part of her livelihood from Grandfather's smallholding* (which she had in fact managed during his illness) for as long as she liked, or until she married again, which was not likely, since no one knew whether my father was alive or dead.

It was when they reached the personal effects* that we got a surprise, for my grandfather had left his watch to me!

'Why your Will?' my Uncle Henry asked in surly* tones. 'I've two lads o' me own and both older than Will.'

'An' neither of 'em ever seemed to know their grandfather was poorly*,' my mother retorted, sharp as a knife.

'Young an' old don't mix,' Uncle Henry muttered, and my mother, thoroughly ruffled*, snapped back, 'Well Will an' his grandfather mixed very nicely, and your father was right glad of his company when there wasn't so much of anybody else's.'

This shot got home on Uncle Henry, who had been a poor sick-visitor. It never took my family long to work up a row and listening from the kitchen through the partly open door, I waited for some real north-country family sparring*. But my Uncle John, Grandfather's eldest son, and a fair man, chipped in* and put a stop to it. 'Now that's enough,' he rumbled in his deep voice. 'We'll have no wranglin'* wi' the old man hardly in his coffin.' There was a short pause and I could imagine him looking round at everyone. 'I'd a fancy for that watch meself*, but me father knew what he was about an' if he chose to leave it young Will, then I'm not goin' to argue about it.' And that was the end of it; the watch was mine.

The house seemed very strange without my grandfather and during the half-hour after tea, when it had been my custom to sit with him, I felt for a long time greatly at a loss. The watch had a lot to do with this feeling. I still admired it in the late afternoon but now it hung by the mantelshelf* in the kitchen where I had persuaded my mother to let it be. My grandfather and his watch had always been inseparable in my mind, and to see the watch without at the same time seeing him was to feel keenly the awful finality of his going. The new position of the watch was in the nature of a compromise between my mother and me. While it was officially mine, it was being held in trust* by my mother until she considered me old enough and careful enough to look after it. She was all for putting it away till that time, but I protested so strongly that she finally agreed to keep it in the kitchen where I could see it all the time, taking care, however, to have it away in a drawer when any of the family were expected, because, she said, there was no point in 'rubbing it in.*'

The holidays came to an end and it was time for me to start my first term at the Grammar School in Cressley. A host of new excitements came to fill my days. I was cast into the melting pot* of the first form* and I had to work for my position in that new fraternity* along with twenty odd other boys from all parts of the town. Friendships were made in those first weeks which would last into adult life. One formed first opinions about one's fellows, and one had one's own label stuck on according to the first impression made. For first impressions seemed vital, and it looked as though the boy who was lucky or clever enough to assert himself favourably at the start would have an advantage for the rest of his schooldays.

There are many ways in which a boy – or a man – may try to establish himself with his fellows. One or two of my classmates grovelled* at everyone's feet, while others took the opposite line and tried systematically to beat the form into submission*, starting with the smallest boy and working up till they met their match. Others charmed everyone by their skill at sports, and others by simply being themselves and seeming hardly to make any effort at all. I have never made friends easily and I was soon branded as aloof*. For a time I did little more than get on speaking terms with my fellows.

One of our number was the youngest son of a well-to-do local tradesman and he had a brother who was a prefect* in the sixth*. His way of asserting himself was to parade his possessions before our envious eyes; and while these tactics did not win him popularity they gained him a certain following and made him one of the most discussed members of the form.

Crawley's bicycle was brand new and had a three-speed gear, an oil-bath gearcase, a speedometer, and other desirable refinements. Crawley's fountain pen matched his propelling pencil and had a gold nib. His football boots were of the best hide* and his gym slippers* were reinforced with rubber across the toes. Everything, in fact, that Crawley had was better than ours. Until he brought the watch.

He flashed it on his wrist with arrogant pride, making a great show of looking at the time. His eldest brother had brought it from abroad. He'd even smuggled it through the customs especially for him. Oh, yes, said Crawley, it had a sweep second-hand* and luminous* figures, and wasn't it absolutely the finest watch we had ever seen? But I was thinking of my grandfather's watch: my watch now. There had never been a watch to compare with that. With heart-thumping excitement I found myself cutting in on Crawley's self-satisfied eulogy*.

'I've seen a better watch than that.'

'Gerraway*!'

'Yes I have,' I insisted. 'It was my grandfather's. He left it to me when he died.'

'Well show us it,' Crawley said.

'I haven't got it here.'

'You haven't got it at all,' Crawley said. 'You can't show us it to prove it.'

I could have knocked the sneer* from his hateful face in rage that he could doubt the worth of the watch for which my grandfather had worked fifty years.

'I'll bring it this afternoon,' I said; 'then you'll see!'

The hand of friendship was extended tentatively* in my direction several times that morning. I should not be alone in my pleasure at seeing Crawley taken down a peg*. As the clock moved with maddening slowness to half-past twelve I thought with grim glee* of how in one move I would settle Crawley's boasting and assert myself with my fellows. On the bus going home, however, I began to wonder how on earth I was going to persuade my mother to let me take the watch out of doors. But I had forgotten that today was Monday, washing day, when my mother put my grandfather's watch in a drawer, away from the steam. I had only to wait for her to step outside for a moment and I could slip the watch into my pocket. She would not miss it before I came home for tea. And if she did, it would be too late.

I was too eager and excited to wait for the return bus and after dinner I got my bike out of the shed. My mother watched me from the kitchen doorway and I could imagine her keen eyes piercing the cloth of my blazer* to where the watch rested guiltily in my pocket.

'Are you going on your bike, then, Will?'

I said, 'Yes, Mother,' and, feeling uncomfortable under that direct gaze, began to wheel the bike across the yard.

'I thought you said it needed mending or something before you rode it again . . .?'

'It's only a little thing,' I told her. 'It'll be all right.'

I waved good-bye and pedalled out into the street while she watched me, a little doubtfully, I thought. Once out of sight of the house I put all my strength on the pedals and rode like the wind. My grandfather's house was in one of the older parts of the town and my way led through a maze of steep cobbled* streets between long rows of houses. I kept up my speed, excitement coursing* through me as I thought of the watch and revelled in* my hatred of Crawley. Then from an entry between two terraces of houses a mongrel puppy darted into the street. I pulled at my back brake. The cable snapped with a click – that was what I had intended to fix. I jammed on the front brake with the puppy cowering* foolishly in my path. The bike jarred to a standstill, the back end swinging as though catapulted* over the pivot* of the stationary front wheel, and I went over the handlebars.

A man picked me up out of the gutter*. 'All right, lad?'

I nodded uncertainly. I seemed unhurt. I rubbed my knees and the side on which I had fallen. I felt the outline of the watch. Sick apprehension* overcame me, but I waited till I was round the next corner before dismounting again and putting a trembling hand into my pocket. Then I looked down at what was left of my grandfather's proudest possession. There was a

deep bulge in the back of the case. The glass was shattered and
the Roman numerals looked crazily at one another across the
pierced and distorted face. I put the watch back in my pocket
and rode slowly on, my mind numb with misery.

I thought of showing them what was left; but that was no
use. I had promised them a prince among watches and no
amount of beautiful wreckage would do.

'Where's the watch, Will?' they asked. 'Have you brought
the watch?'

'My mother wouldn't let me bring it,' I lied, moving to my
desk, my hand in my pocket clutching the shattered watch.

'His mother wouldn't let him,' Crawley jeered*. 'What a
tale!'

(Later, Crawley, I thought. The day will come.)

The others took up his cries. I was branded as a romancer, a
fanciful liar. I couldn't blame them after letting them down.

The bell rang for first class and I sat quietly at my desk,
waiting for the master to arrive. I opened my books and stared
blindly at them as a strange feeling stole over me. It was not the
mocking of my classmates – they would tire of that eventually. Nor was it the thought of my mother's anger, terrible
though that would be. No, all I could think of – all that possessed my mind – was the old man, my grandfather, lying in
his bed after a long life of toil, his hands fretting with the
sheets, and his tired, breathy voice saying, 'Patience, Will,
patience.'

And I nearly wept, for it was the saddest moment of my
young life.

Glossary

The meanings given below are those which the words and phrases have as they occur in the story.

Page

31   *chased*: decorated with markings.

drawing near his time: approaching the time when he would die.

braille: system of raised dots on paper which allow blind people to read by touch.

an ounce of twist: a small quantity of pipe tobacco.

Grammar School: type of British school that provides a more academic education to children over the age of 11.

pleased as Punch: very pleased.

he will (dial.): Will's grandfather uses 'he' rather than 'you' when talking to his grandson.

32   *Yorkshire*: a county (large administrative area) in northern England.

cornerstones: foundations, things of greatest importance.

t'way (dial.): the way. The Yorkshire dialect often reduces 'the' to 't'.

fidgeted: made nervous restless movements with his fingers.

gettin' on: getting late.

hisself (dial.): himself (Grandfather is still referring to Will).

covet: want to own.

wa' gi'n (dial.): was given.

theer (dial.): there.

blacksmith: a man who makes and repairs things made of iron, especially someone who makes horseshoes.

tongs: a metal instrument used by a blacksmith for holding or lifting heavy (metal) objects.

shrouded: covered, hidden.

32   *perserverance*: constant effort.

reviling: speaking strongly and angrily about.

gone astray: got into wrong ways.

laid him out: arranged the dead body before the burial.

mustiness: unpleasant smell of old things.

scores: large number.

fretting: continuously moving in a nervous way.

in force: in large numbers.

34 *smallholding*: small piece of farmland.

personal effects: personal property.

surly: bad-tempered, unfriendly.

poorly (dial.): ill.

ruffled: angered.

sparring: angry argument.

chipped in: suddenly interrupted the conversation.

wranglin': (wrangling) angry arguing.

meself (dial.): myself.

mantelshelf: small shelf above the fireplace.

35 *held in trust*: property held and managed by one person for another.

rubbing it in (coll.): reminding people of something they would prefer to forget.

cast into the melting pot: thrown into a place where different types of people are mixed together.

first form (Br.E.): first class in the grammar school (for children aged about 11).

fraternity: society of schoolboys.

grovelled: acted in a way that was shamefully humble and eager to please.

beat . . . submission: fight the others so that they would be obeyed.

branded as aloof: given a bad name as someone who is unfriendly and distant.

prefect (Br.E.): an older pupil who keeps order over other pupils.

the sixth (Br.E): the last class at school (for pupils aged about 17–18).

36 *hide*: leather.

gym slippers: light shoes used for sports and gymnastics.

sweep second-hand: moving watch hand that gives the seconds.

luminous: can be seen in the dark.

eulogy: speech of praise.

Gerraway (dial.): Get away! i.e. I do not believe you.

sneer: unpleasant expression of pride and dislike.

The hand . . . tentatively: friendship was offered in a hesitant and experimental way.

taken down a peg (coll.): humbled, shown he was not as important as he thought he was.

grim glee: pleased and satisfied in a rather cruel and hard way.

37 *blazer*: schoolboy's jacket.

cobbled: streets made of rounded stones.

coursing: flowing quickly.

revelled: enjoyed greatly.

cowering: drawing back in fear.

catapulted: suddenly and quickly thrown.

pivot: fixed central point.

gutter: the part of the road near the pavement (where people walk).

apprehension: fear about what might come next.

38 *jeered*: laughed in an unpleasant way.

Questions

1. How is the theme of patience introduced and developed in the story?

   (a) Where is the first mention of 'patience'? Who mentions it? (p. 31)

   (b) What are the cornerstones of Grandfather's life? (p. 32)

   (c) Will's father was 'impatient to make money, to be a success, to impress his friends'. (p. 33) What parts of the story show that Will is similar to his father? (pp. 35–36)

   (d) When Grandfather is dying his fingers are 'restless', and Will comments, 'I believe he came as near to losing his patience then as at any time in his long life' (p. 33) – losing his patience with what?

(e) Why does Will take the bike back to school rather than the bus? (p. 37)

(f) Why at the end of the story is the thought of his Grandfather more painful to Will than the mocking of his schoolmates or the anger of his mother? (p. 38)

2. Why is the watch important in the story?

(a) In the first paragraph Barstow writes 'The mechanism . . . gave such a deep, steady ticking that you could not imagine its ever going wrong'. (p. 31) In what ways is Grandfather 'steady'? In what way could it be said that Grandfather is now 'going wrong'?

(b) Why was the watch given Grandfather? (p. 32)

(c) Why did Grandfather give Will the watch when he could have given it to older and closer members of the family? (pp. 32–4)

(d) 'I felt for a long time greatly at a loss. The watch had a lot to do with the feeling'. (p. 34) In what ways are the watch and Grandfather associated for Will?

(e) Look at the passage from 'Then I looked down . . .' to '. . . beautiful wreckage would do' (p. 38). Make a list of the positive words (e.g. 'proudest' etc.) and the negative words (e.g. 'bulge' etc.). Why are there so many negative words at this point in the story?

Language Activities

Differences in meaning

Below is the ending of Barstow's 'One of the Virtues'. For each item (1–8) you have three alternatives. In each item circle the *one* alternative you think the author chose.

The bell rang for first class and I sat (1. *peacefully/quietly/anxiously*) at my desk, waiting for the master to arrive. I opened my books and stared (2. *inattentively/absent-mindedly/blindly*) at them as a strange feeling stole over me. It was not the (3. *giggling/laughing/mocking*) of my classmates – they would tire of that eventually. Nor was it the thought of my mother's (4. *irritation/anger/annoyance*), terrible though that would be. No, all I could think of – all that (5. *possessed/occupied/was in*) my mind – was the old man, my grandfather, lying in his bed after a long life of (6. *manual labour/toil/work*), his hands fretting with the sheets, and his (7. *tired/sleepy/exhausted*), breathy voice saying, 'Patience, Will, patience.'

And I nearly (8. *cried/wept/started crying*), for it was the saddest moment of my young life.

Compare your answers with the text. If your choice was different from the author's, what is the difference in meaning between your choice and the author's?

The structure of the story

Arrange the following fourteen stages in the story into the correct order. Writing down the stages and cutting them up separately will help you to do this activity.

1. Will's bicycle accident with the watch.
2. Details about how schoolboys try to win popularity.
3. Will branded as a liar by his schoolfriends.
4. Argument over the will.
5. Details given about Will's father.
6. The idea of patience first introduced.
7. The last mention of the idea of patience.
8. Description of the watch over Grandfather's bed.
9. Details given about Will sitting by his Grandfather's bed.
10. Details of Grandfather's job as a blacksmith.
11. Crawley's boasting.
12. Will gets the watch in his Grandfather's will.
13. The watch put in the kitchen.
14. Grandfather's death.

Check your answers with the text, noting the points at which a new stage is introduced.

Ideas for Writing

1. Rearrange the stages given in *The Structure of the Story* so that the order is different from that found in Barstow's story (you could, for example, start with the bicycle accident or have Grandfather die after the bicycle accident). Write out this story in your own words. You may leave out certain stages if you wish.

2. Imagine that the bicycle accident does not smash the watch. Write an alternative ending to the story to follow on from this: 'I waited till I was round the next corner before dismounting again and putting a trembling hand into my pocket. I took it out. There it shone in the sun, as beautiful as ever . . .'

Frank O'Connor (1903–66)

Frank O'Connor was born in Cork in Southern Ireland and came from a poor family. He could not afford to go to university and was largely self-educated. He began to write at an early age, working as a librarian to maintain himself. His reputation is based on his short stories, his first collection, *Guests of the Nation*, appearing in 1931, to be followed by several more collections including *My Oedipus Complex and Other Stories*, semi-autobiographical stories of Irish life which, like 'The Man of the House', deal with O'Connor's childhood and in particular with the close relationship he had with his adoring mother.

Apart from short stories, O'Connor has also written verse, three books about Ireland and several books of literary criticism. *The Lonely Voice* (1963), a critical work on the short story, is particularly interesting.

The story

'It's a funny thing about women, the way they'll take orders from anything in trousers, even if it's only ten.'

Set in Cork, O'Connor's birthplace, 'The Man of the House' is the story of a ten-year-old boy who does, for a time, take wonderful care of his mother while she is ill in bed. However, after a while the responsibility gets a little too much for him . . .

The Man of the House

W HEN I woke, I heard my mother coughing, below in the kitchen. She had been coughing for days, but I had paid no attention. We were living on the Old Youghal Road* at the time, the old hilly coaching road* into East Cork*. The coughing sounded terrible. I dressed and went downstairs in my stocking feet, and in the clear morning light I saw her, unaware that she was being watched, collapsed into a little wickerwork* armchair, holding her side. She had made an attempt to light the fire, but it had gone against her. She looked so tired and helpless that my heart turned over with compassion*. I ran to her.

'Are you all right, Mum?' I asked.

'I'll be all right in a second,' she replied, trying to smile. 'The old sticks were wet, and the smoke started me coughing.'

'Go back to bed and I'll light the fire,' I said.

'Ah, how can I, child?' she said anxiously. 'Sure*, I have to go to work.'

'You couldn't work like that,' I said. 'I'll stop at home from school and look after you.'

It's a funny thing about women, the way they'll take orders from anything in trousers, even if it's only ten.

'If you could make yourself a cup of tea, I might be all right later on,' she said guiltily, and she rose, very shakily, and climbed back up the stairs. I knew then she must be feeling really bad.

I got more sticks out of the coalhole, under the stairs. My mother was so economical that she never used enough, and that was why the fire sometimes went against her. I used a whole bundle, and I soon had the fire roaring and the kettle on. I made her toast while I was about it. I was a great believer in hot buttered toast at all hours of the day. Then I made the tea and brought her up a cup on the tray. 'Is that all right?' I asked.

'Would you have a sup* of boiling water left?' she asked doubtfully.

' 'Tis too strong,' I agreed cheerfully, remembering the patience of the saints in their many afflictions*. 'I'll pour half of it out.'

'I'm an old nuisance,' she sighed.

' 'Tis my fault,' I said, taking the cup. 'I can never remember about tea. Put the shawl* round you while you're sitting up. Will I* shut the skylight*?'

'Would you be able?' she asked doubtfully.

' 'Tis no trouble,' I said, getting the chair to it. 'I'll do the messages* after.'

I had my own breakfast alone by the window, and then I went out and stood by the front door to watch the kids from the road on their way to school.

'You'd better hurry or you'll be killed*, Sullivan,' they shouted.

'I'm not going,' I said. 'My mother is sick, and I have to mind* the house.'

I wasn't a malicious child, by any means, but I liked to be able to take out my comforts and study them by the light of others' misfortunes. Then I heated another kettle of water and cleared up the breakfast things before I washed my face and came up to the attic* with my shopping basket, a piece of paper, and a lead pencil.

'I'll do the messages now if you'll write them down,' I said. 'Would you like me to get the doctor?'

'Ah,' said my mother impatiently, 'he'd only want to send me to hospital, and how would I go to hospital? You could call in at the chemist's and ask him to give you a good, strong cough bottle.'

'Write it down,' I said. 'If I haven't it written down, I might forget it. And put 'strong' in big letters. What will I get for the dinner? Eggs?'

As boiled eggs were the only dish I could manage, I more or less knew it would be eggs, but she told me to get sausages as well, in case she could get up.

I passed the school on my way. Opposite it was a hill, and I went up a short distance and stood there for ten minutes in quiet contemplation. The schoolhouse and yard and gate were revealed as in a painted picture, detached and peaceful except for the chorus of voices through the opened windows and the glimpse of Danny Delaney, the teacher, passing the front door with his cane* behind his back, stealing a glance at the world outside. I could have stood there all day. Of all the profound and simple pleasures of those days, that was the richest.

When I got home, I rushed upstairs and found Minnie Ryan sitting with my mother. She was a middle-aged woman, very knowledgeable, gossipy, and pious.

'How are you, Mum?' I asked.

'Grand,' said my mother, with a smile.

'You can't get up today, though,' said Minnie Ryan.

'I'll put the kettle on and make a cup of tea for you,' I said.

'Sure, I'll do that,' said Minnie.

'Ah, don't worry, Miss Ryan,' I said lightly. 'I can manage it all right.'

'Wisha*, isn't he very good?' I heard her say in a low voice to my mother.

'As good as gold,' said my mother.

'There's not many like that, then,' said Minnie. 'The most of them that's going now are more like savages than Christians.'

In the afternoon, my mother wanted me to run out and play, but I didn't go far. I knew if once I went a certain distance from the house, I was liable to stray into temptation*. Below our house, there was a glen*, the drill field of the barracks* perched high above it on a chalky cliff, and below, in a deep hollow, the millpond and millstream running between wooded hills – the Rockies, the Himalayas, or the Highlands, according to your mood*. Once down there, I tended to forget the real world, so I sat on a wall outside the house, running in every half hour to see how the mother was and if there was anything she wanted.

Evening fell; the street lamps were lit, and the paper boy went crying* up the road. I bought a paper, lit the lamp in the kitchen and the candle in my mother's attic, and tried to read to her, not very successfully, because I was only at words of one syllable, but I had a great wish to please, and she to be pleased, so we got on quite well, considering.

Later, Minnie Ryan came again, and as she was going, I saw her to the door.

'If she's not better in the morning, I think I'd get the doctor, Flurry,' she said, over her shoulder.

'Why?' I asked, in alarm. 'Do you think is she worse, Miss Ryan?'

'Ah, I wouldn't say so,' she replied with affected nonchalance*, 'but I'd be frightened she might get pneumonia*.'

'But wouldn't he send her to hospital, Miss Ryan?'

'Wisha, he mightn't,' she said with a shrug, pulling her old shawl about her. 'But even if he did, wouldn't it be better than neglecting it? Ye wouldn't have a drop of whiskey in the house?'

'I'll get it,' I said at once. I knew what might happen to people who got pneumonia, and what was bound to happen afterward to their children.

'If you could give it to her hot, with a squeeze of lemon in it, it might help her to shake it off,' said Minnie.

My mother said she didn't want the whiskey, dreading the expense, but I had got such a fright that I wouldn't be put off. When I went to the public house, it was full of men, who drew aside to let me reach the bar. I had never been in a public house before, and I was frightened.

'Hullo, my old flower*,' said one man, grinning diabolically* at me. 'It must be ten years since I seen you last. What are you having*?'

My pal, Bob Connell, had told me how he once asked a drunk man for a half crown and the man gave it to him. I always wished I could bring myself to do the same, but I didn't feel like it just then.

'I want a half glass of whiskey for my mother,' I said.

'Oh, the thundering ruffian!' said the man. 'Pretending 'tis for his mother, and the last time I seen him he had to be carried home.'

'I had not,' I shouted indignantly. 'And *'tis* for my mother. She's sick.'

'Ah, let the child alone, Johnnie,' said the barmaid. She gave me the whiskey, and then, still frightened of the men in the public house, I went off to a shop for a lemon.

When my mother had drunk the hot whiskey, she fell asleep; and I quenched the lights and went to bed, but I couldn't sleep very well. I was regretting I hadn't asked the man in the pub for a half crown. I was wakened several times by the coughing, and when I went into my mother's room her head felt very hot, and she was rambling* in her talk. It frightened me more than anything else when she didn't know me, and I lay awake, thinking of what would happen to me if it were really pneumonia.

The depression was terrible when, next morning, my mother seemed not to be any better. I had done all I could do, and I felt helpless. I lit the fire and got her breakfast, but this time I didn't stand at the front door to see the other fellows on their way to school. I should have been too inclined to envy them. Instead, I went over to Minnie Ryan and reported.

'I'd go for the doctor,' she said firmly. 'Better be sure than sorry.'

I had first to go to the house of a Poor Law Guardian*, for a ticket to show we couldn't pay. Then I went down to the dispensary*, which was in a deep hollow beyond the school. After that I had to go back to ready the house for the doctor. I had to have a basin of water and soap and a clean towel laid out for him, and I had to get the dinner, too.

It was after dinner when he called. He was a fat, loud-voiced man and, like all the drunks of the medical profession, supposed to be 'the cleverest doctor in Cork, if only he'd mind himself.' He hadn't been minding himself much that morning, it seemed.

'How are you going to get this now?' he grumbled, sitting on the bed with the prescription pad* on his knee. 'The only place open is the North Dispensary.'

'I'll go, Doctor,' I said at once, relieved that he had said nothing about hospital.

' 'Tis a long way,' he said, doubtfully. 'Do you know where it is?'

'I'll find it,' I said.

'Isn't he a great little fellow?' he said to my mother.

'Oh, the best in the world, Doctor!' she said. 'A daughter couldn't be better to me.'

'That's right,' said the doctor. 'Look after your mother; she'll be the best for you in the long run. We don't mind them when we have them,' he added, to my mother, 'and then we spend the rest of our lives regretting it.'

I wished he hadn't said that; it tuned in altogether too well with my mood. To make it worse, he didn't even use the soap and water I had laid ready for him.

My mother gave me directions how to reach the dispensary, and I set off with a bottle wrapped in brown paper under my arm. The road led uphill, through a thickly populated poor locality, as far as the barracks, which was perched on the very top of the hill, over the city, and then descended, between high walls, till it suddenly almost disappeared in a stony path, with red brick corporation houses* to one side of it, that dropped steeply, steeply, to the valley of the little river, where a brewery stood, and the opposite hillside, a murmuring honeycomb* of houses, rose to the gently rounded top, on which stood the purple sandstone tower of the cathedral and the limestone spire of Shandon church, on a level with your eye.

It was so wide a view that it was never all lit up together, and the sunlight wandered across it as across a prairie*, picking out first a line of roofs with a brightness like snow, and then delving into* the depth of some dark street and outlining in shadow figures of climbing carts and straining horses. I leaned on the low wall and thought how happy a fellow could be, looking at that, if he had nothing to trouble him. I tore myself from it with a sigh, slithered without stopping to the bottom of the hill, and climbed up a series of shadowy and stepped lanes around the back of the cathedral, which now seemed enormous. I had a penny, which my mother had given me by way of encouragement, and I made up my mind that when I had done my business, I should go into the cathedral and spend it on a candle to the Blessed Virgin*, to make my mother better quick. I felt sure it would be more effective in a really big church like that, so very close to Heaven.

The dispensary was a sordid* little hallway with a bench to one side and a window like the one in a railway ticket office at the far end. There was a little girl with a green plaid shawl about her shoulders sitting on the bench. I knocked at the window, and a seedy*, angry-looking man opened it. Without waiting for me to finish what I was saying, he grabbed bottle and prescription from me and banged the shutter down again without a word. I waited for a moment and then lifted my hand to knock again.

'You'll have to wait, little boy,' said the girl quickly.

'What will I have to wait for?' I asked.

'He have* to make it up,' she explained. 'You might as well sit down.'

I did, glad of anyone to keep me company.

'Where are you from?' she asked. 'I live in Blarney Lane,' she added when I had told her. 'Who's the bottle for?'

'My mother,' I said.

'What's wrong with her?'

'She have a bad cough.'

'She might have consumption*,' she said thoughtfully. 'That's what my sister that died last year had. This is a tonic* for my other sister. She have to have tonics all the time. Is it nice where you live?'

I told her about the glen, and then she told me about the river near their place. It seemed to be a nicer place than ours, as she described it. She was a pleasant, talkative little girl, and I didn't notice the time until the window opened again and a red bottle was thrust out.

'Dooley!' shouted the seedy man, and closed the window again.

'That's me,' said the little girl. 'Yours won't be ready for a good while yet. I'll wait for you.'

'I have a penny,' I said boastfully.

She waited until my bottle was thrust out, and then she accompanied me as far as the steps leading down to the brewery. On the way, I bought a pennyworth of sweets, and we sat on the other steps, beside the infirmary*, to eat them. It was nice there, with the spire of Shandon in shadow behind us, the young trees overhanging the high walls, and the sun, when it came out in great golden blasts, throwing our linked shadows onto the road.

'Give us a taste of your bottle, little boy,' she said.

'Why?' I asked. 'Can't you taste your own?'

'Mine is awful,' she said. 'Tonics is* awful to taste. You can try it if you like.'

I took a taste of it and hastily spat out. She was right; it was awful. After that, I couldn't do less than let her taste mine.

'That's grand,' she said enthusiastically, after taking a swig* from it. 'Cough bottles are nearly always grand. Try it, can't you?'

I did, and saw she was right about that, too. It was very sweet and sticky.

'Give us another,' she said excitedly, grabbing at it.

' 'Twill be all gone,' I said.

'Erra, 'twon't*,' she replied with a laugh. 'You have gallons of it.'

Somehow, I couldn't refuse her. I was swept from my anchorage* into an unfamiliar world of spires and towers, trees, steps, shadowy laneways, and little girls with red hair and green eyes. I took a drink myself and gave her another. Then I began to panic. ' 'Tis nearly gone,' I said. 'What am I going to do now?'

'Finish it and say the cork fell out,' she replied, and again, as she said it, it sounded plausible* enough. We finished the bottle between us, and then, slowly, as I looked at it in my hand, empty as I had brought it, and remembered that I had not kept my word to the Blessed Virgin and had spent her penny on sweets, a terrible despondency* swept over me. I had sacrificed everything for the little girl and she didn't even care for me. It was my cough bottle she had coveted* all the time. I saw her guile* too late. I put my head in my hands and began to cry.

'What are you crying for?' the little girl asked in astonishment.

'My mother is sick, and we're after drinking* her medicine,' I said.

'Ah, don't be an old crybaby!' she said contemptuously*. 'You have only to say the cork fell out. Sure, that's a thing could happen to anybody.'

'And I promised the Blessed Virgin a candle, and I spent the money on you!' I screamed, and, suddenly grabbing the empty bottle, I ran up the road from her, wailing*. Now I had only one refuge and one hope – a miracle*. I went back to the cathedral, and, kneeling before the shrine* of the Blessed Virgin, I begged her pardon for having spent her penny, and promised her a candle from the next penny I got, if only she would work a miracle and make my mother better before I got back. After that, I crawled miserably homeword, back up the great hill, but now all the light had gone out of the day, and the murmuring hillside had become a vast*, alien*, cruel world. Besides, I felt very sick. I thought I might be going to die. In one way it would be better.

When I got back into the house, the silence of the kitchen and then the sight of the fire gone out in the grate* smote me* with the cruel realization that the Blessed Virgin had let me down. There was no miracle, and my mother was still in bed. At once, I began to howl*.

'What is it at all, child?' she call in alarm from upstairs.

'I lost the medicine,' I bellowed*, and rushed up the stairs to throw myself on the bed and bury my face in the clothes.

'Oh, wisha, if that's all that's a trouble to you!' she exclaimed with relief, running her hand through my hair. 'Is anything the matter?' she added, after a moment. 'You're very hot.'

'I drank the medicine,' I bawled.

'Ah, what harm?' she murmured soothingly. 'You poor, unfortunate child! 'Twas my own fault for letting you go all that way by yourself. And then to have your journey for nothing. Undress yourself now, and you can lie down here.'

She got up, put on her slippers and coat, and unlaced my boots while I sat on the bed. But even before she had finished I was fast asleep. I didn't see her dress herself or hear her go out, but some time later I felt a hand on my forehead and saw

Minnie Ryan peering down at me, laughing.

'Ah, 'twill be nothing,' she said, giving her shawl a pull about her. 'He'll sleep it off by morning. The dear* knows, Mrs Sullivan, 'tis you should be in bed.'

I knew that was a judgement on me, but I could do nothing about it. Later I saw my mother come in with the candle and her paper, and I smiled up at her. She smiled back. Minnie Ryan might despise me as much as she liked, but there were others who didn't. The miracle had happened, after all.

Glossary

The meanings given below are those which the words and phrases have as they occur in the story.

Page

47 *Old Youghal Road*: Youghal is a town in Southern Ireland.

coaching road: at one time a road for horse-drawn carriages.

Cork: a city in Southern Ireland.

wickerwork: the armchair is made of thin sticks of wood woven together.

compassion: pity.

Sure (Irish coll.): a common interjection. Here it means something like 'Don't you know . . .'

sup (Irish coll.): a mouthful.

48 *remembering. . .afflictions*: the meaning here is that the holy saints suffered troubles without complaining, so he will too.

shawl: large piece of cloth worn over a woman's head or shoulders.

Will I . . . (dial.): Shall I . . .

skylight: window in a roof.

messages (Irish coll.): shopping.

you'll be killed (coll.): the teacher will be very angry.

to mind (coll.): to look after.

attic: room at the top of a house.

49 *cane*: long thin stick used by schoolteachers to hit pupils with.

Wisha (Irish dial.): a mild expression of surprise.

liable. . .temptation: likely to do wrong things (i.e. forget he must take care of his mother).

glen: a narrow valley.

drill field. . .barracks: place where soldiers are trained to handle weapons, march etc. and where they live.

Rockies. . .Highlands. . . mood: the boy could imagine the hills were the American Rocky Mountains, the Himalayas in India or the Scottish Highlands.

went crying: shouted out the name of the newspaper.

50   *affected nonchalance*: pretended lack of interest.

pneumonia: serious disease of the lungs.

my old flower (Irish coll.): a term of affection.

diabolically: in a devilish, evil way.

What are you having?: What do you want to drink? (alcohol).

51   *rambling*: talking in a disordered, disconnected way.

Poor Law Guardian: Until 1930 an official who administered laws that helped the poor (now replaced by social security services).

dispensary: place where medicines are given out.

prescription pad: order forms that a doctor writes on so that a patient can get medicine.

52   *corporation houses*: houses built and owned by the local government of an area.

honeycomb: the houses looked like the cells in which bees make honey.

prairie: wide, flat area of grassland.

delving into: entering into, penetrating.

spend. . .Blessed Virgin: the boy is a member of a Roman Catholic family. Lighting a candle to the Virgin Mary is a way of praying that his sick mother will get better.

53   *sordid*: very dirty and poor-looking.

seedy: looking poor and worn out.

He have (dial.): He has.

consumption: a serious disease that affects especially the lungs.

tonic: a medicine that gives energy and strength.

infirmary: hospital.

54   *Tonics is (dial.)*: Tonics are.

swig (coll.): drink.

Erra, 'twon't (Irish dial.): No, it won't.

anchorage: fixed, safe place.

plausible: reasonable.

despondency: a feeling that all hope is lost.

coveted: wanted to have.

guile: cleverness in tricking, deceiving.

we're after drinking (Irish dial.): we've drunk.

55 *contemptuously*: said without respect as though to a lower person.

wailing: crying noisily.

miracle: a holy event, something that cannot be explained by the laws of nature.

shrine: place of worship.

vast: very large.

alien: foreign.

grate: part of the fireplace where wood, coal etc. is placed.

smote me: hit me hard.

howl: cry noisily.

bellowed: shouted loudly and unhappily.

56 *The dear (Irish coll.)*: The dear Lord, God.

Questions

1. What is the importance of the boy's imagination in the story?

   (a) Why does the boy like watching his friends going to school the first morning his mother is ill? (p. 48)

   (b) When going shopping, the boy looks at the school and says 'I could have stood there all day'. (p. 49) Why?

   (c) On the first afternoon, the mother wants the boy to 'run out and play'. Why does he not go far? What does he mean by 'I tended to forget the real world'? (p. 49)

   (d) When fetching the medicine, he stops to look at the city and says 'I tore myself from it with a sigh.' Why doesn't he want to leave it? (p. 52)

   (e) The narrator says he could not refuse to give the girl his medicine because 'I was swept from my anchorage into the unfamiliar world of spires and towers, trees, steps, shadowy laneways, and little girls with red hair and green eyes'. (p. 54) Explain what you understand by these words.

2. What religious and biblical elements are there in the story?

(a) The boy decides to spend the penny his mother had given him on a candle. Why does he decide to light this candle in the cathedral rather than an ordinary church? (pp. 52–3)

(b) What is the 'miracle' that he prays for in the cathedral? (p. 55)

(c) The last sentence says that the 'miracle' does in fact happen. Does the writer just mean that the mother seems to be well again, or does he mean something more? (p. 56)

(d) In the biblical story Adam is tempted by Eve so that they both fall into sin. How is the story of the boy and the little girl similar?

3. How are serious and comic elements combined in the story?

(a) Minnie Ryan suggests that the mother may get pneumonia, and the boy's thoughts are given: 'I knew what might happen to people who got pneumonia, and what was bound to happen to their children.' (p. 50) What does the boy imagine might happen to his mother and to him?

(b) Immediately after these thoughts the boy goes to the pub. What comic meeting takes place here? (pp. 50–1)

(c) The doctor warns the boy about what would happen if he didn't take care of his mother. (p. 52) What would happen? What does the boy think of the doctor's words? In what way does he not look after his mother properly later?

(d) The little girl talks about consumption and her sister's death. (p. 53) How seriously does she discuss these matters?

(e) Why is the little girl so knowledgeable about the tastes of different medicines? (pp. 53–4)

(f) After his prayers are unanswered at the cathedral the boy feels that the world is 'vast, alien, cruel' (p. 55) and then immediately adds 'Besides, I felt very sick'. How seriously do you take the boy's sense of tragedy?

Language Activities

Seriousness and Comedy

O'Connor is very successful at getting inside the mind and imagination of a child. The boy in the story takes life very seriously, but when reading the story we may sometimes feel that the boy's sense of the tragedy of life (at one point he calls the world 'cruel') is rather exaggerated and is even rather funny.

In the following excerpts from the story an everyday detail or thought is introduced which provides a comic contrast with what has gone before. Underline these sentences.

(a) 'That's right,' said the doctor. 'Look after your mother: she'll be the best for you in the long run. We don't mind them when we have them,' he added, to my mother, 'and then we spend the rest of our lives regretting it.' I wished he hadn't said that: it tuned in altogether too well with my mood. To make it worse, he didn't even use the soap and water I laid ready for him. (p. 52)

(b) . . . a terrible despondency swept over me. I had sacrificed everything for the little girl and she didn't care for me. It was my cough bottle she had coveted all the time. (p. 54)

(c) . . . I crawled miserably homeward, back up the great hill, but now all the light had gone out of the day, and the murmuring hillside had become a vast, alien, cruel world. Besides, I felt very sick. (p. 55)

(d) When I got back into the house, the silence of the kitchen and then the sight of the fire gone out in the grate smote me with the cruel realization that the Blessed Virgin had let me down. There was no miracle, and my mother was still in bed. At once I began to howl. (p. 55)

Religious and Moral Words

Not unsurprisingly in a story of an Irish boy growing up in a Roman Catholic family, there are many references to churches, religion and morality: *spire, cathedral, Blessed Virgin, pious* etc.

Sometimes in the story O'Connor even uses words with religious meanings in situations which are not religious, e.g. drinking a cup of tea or meeting a man in a pub. This is one way O'Connor keeps the reader's mind on the fact that this story deals with the moral themes of temptation, sin and guilt.

In the following underline the word or words that have religious or moral associations.

(a) '[The tea is] . . . too strong,' I agreed cheerfully, remembering the patience of the saints in their many afflictions. (p. 48)

(b) In the afternoon, my mother wanted me to run out and play, but I didn't go far. I knew if once I went a certain distance from the house, I was liable to stray into temptation. (p. 49)

(c) [In a pub] 'Hullo, my old flower,' said one man, grinning diabolically at me. 'It must be ten years since I seen you last.' (p. 50)

(d) I had sacrificed everything for the little girl and she didn't even care for me. It was my cough bottle she had coveted all the time. I saw her guile too late. (p. 54)

(e) Minnie Ryan might despise me as much as she liked, but there were others who didn't. The miracle had happened, after all. (p. 56)

Ideas for Writing

1. Write a story about childhood guilt (a child's theft of money/sweets from a sweet shop: a child hiding the fact that he or she has broken an expensive vase etc.)

2. Write an alternative ending to the story to follow on from this: 'When I got back into the house, the silence of the kitchen and then the sight of the fire gone out in the grate smote me with the cruel realization that the Blessed Virgin

had let me down. There was no miracle, and my mother was still in bed. In fact she was worse . . .'

* * * * * *

1. Which of these two stories do you prefer? What are some of the reasons for your choice?

2. Both the stories are about ten-year-old boys. Do the boys seem similar to you? What are some of their similarities and differences?

3. Do you think the events given in the stories will have an effect on the future lives of the boys? Try to imagine what they will be like when they get older.

4. Does one of the stories give a fuller picture of the mother than the other? What are some of the differences or similarities between the mothers?

Decision

Graham Greene

Graham Greene was born in 1904 and is regarded as one of Britain's leading writers. He has travelled widely throughout the world, and this is shown in his works. *The Power and the Glory* (1940), for example, is about a 'whisky priest' in Mexico, *The Quiet American* (1955) takes place in Vietnam during the war with the French, and *A Burnt Out Case* (1961) is set in the Congo. Greene's novels often explore the world of crime, spying, war and violent death, but he has also written comedies such as *Our Man in Havana* (1958) and *Travels with My Aunt* (1969), both of which have been filmed. In addition to his novels, Greene has also written plays and several volumes of short stories.

'A Shocking Accident' comes from one of Greene's later collections of short stories, *May We Borrow Your Husband?* (1967), and it deals with an apparently serious subject (a shocking accident) in a humorous way.

The story

Jerome is just nine when he is told about his father's shocking accident. Everybody else, however, seems to find it rather funny . . .

A Shocking Accident

J EROME was called into his housemaster's* room in the break between the second and the third class on a Thursday morning. He had no fear of trouble, for he was a warden – the name that the proprietor* and headmaster of a rather expensive preparatory school* had chosen to give to approved, reliable boys in the lower forms (from a warden one became a guardian and finally before leaving, it was hoped for Marlborough or Rugby*, a crusader). The housemaster, Mr Wordsworth, sat behind his desk with an appearance of perplexity and apprehension*. Jerome had the odd* impression when he entered that he was a cause of fear.

'Sit down, Jerome,' Mr Wordsworth said. 'All going well with the trigonometry*?'

'Yes, sir.'

'I've had a telephone call, Jerome. From your aunt. I'm afraid I have bad news for you.'

'Yes, sir?'

'Your father has had an accident.'

'Oh.'

Mr Wordsworth looked at him with some surprise. 'A serious accident.'

'Yes, sir?'

Jerome worshipped his father: the verb is exact. As man recreates God, so Jerome re-created his father – from a restless widowed* author into a mysterious adventurer who travelled in far places – Nice, Beirut, Majorca, even the Canaries. The time had arrived about his eighth birthday when Jerome believed that his father either 'ran guns*' or was a member of the British Secret Service. Now it occurred to him that his father might have been wounded in 'a hail* of machine-gun bullets'.

Mr Wordsworth played with the ruler on his desk. He

seemed at a loss how to continue. He said, 'You know your father was in Naples?'

'Yes, sir.'

'Your aunt heard from the hospital today.'

'Oh.'

Mr Wordsworth said with desperation. 'It was a street accident.'

'Yes, sir?' It seemed quite likely to Jerome that they would call it a street accident. The police of course had fired first; his father would not take human life except as a last resort*.

'I'm afraid your father was very seriously hurt indeed.'

'Oh.'

'In fact, Jerome, he died yesterday. Quite without pain.'

'Did they shoot him through the heart?'

'I beg your pardon. What did you say, Jerome?'

'Did they shoot him through the heart?'

'Nobody shot him, Jerome. A pig fell on him.' An inexplicable* convulsion* took place in the nerves of Mr Wordsworth's face; it really looked for a moment as though he were going to laugh. He closed his eyes, composed his features and said rapidly as though it were necessary to expel the story as quickly as possible, 'Your father was walking along a street in Naples when a pig fell on him. A shocking accident. Apparently in the poorer quarters* of Naples they keep pigs on their balconies*. This one was on the fifth floor. It had grown too fat. The balcony broke. The pig fell on your father.'

Mr Wordsworth left his desk rapidly and went to the window, turning his back on Jerome. He shook a little with emotion.

Jerome said, 'What happened to the pig?'

[2]

This was not callousness* on the part of Jerome, as it was interpreted by Mr Wordsworth to his colleagues (he even discussed with them whether, perhaps, Jerome was yet fitted to be a warden). Jerome was only attempting to visualize the strange scene to get the details right. Nor was Jerome a boy who cried; he was a boy who brooded* and it never occurred to him at his preparatory school that the circumstances of his father's death were comic – they were still part of the mystery of life. It was later, in his first term at his public school*, when he told the story to his best friend, that he began to realize how it affected others. Naturally after that disclosure* he was known, rather unreasonably, as Pig.

Unfortunately his aunt had no sense of humour. There was an enlarged snapshot* of his father on the piano; a large sad man in an unsuitable dark suit posed in Capri with an umbrella (to guard him against sunstroke), the Faraglione rocks forming the background. By the age of sixteen Jerome was well aware that the portrait looked more like the author of *Sunshine and Shade* and *Rambles* in the Balearics* than an agent of the Secret Service. All the same he loved the memory of his father: he still possessed an album filled with picture-postcards (the stamps had been soaked off long ago for his other collection), and it pained him when his aunt embarked with strangers on the story of his father's death.

'A shocking accident,' she would begin, and the stranger would compose his or her features into the correct shape for interest and commiseration*. Both reactions, of course, were false, but it was terrible for Jerome to see how suddenly, midway in her rambling discourse*, the interest would become genuine. 'I can't think how such things can be allowed in a civilized country,' his aunt would say. 'I suppose one has to regard Italy as civilized. One is prepared for all kinds of things abroad, of course, and my brother was a great traveller. He always carried a water-filter* with him. It was far less expensive, you know, than buying all those bottles of mineral water. My brother always said that his filter paid for his dinner wine. You can see from that what a careful man he was, but who could possibly have expected when he was walking along the Via Dottore Manuele Panucci on his way to the Hydrographic* Museum that a pig would fall on him?' That was the moment when the interest became genuine.

Jerome's father had not been a very distinguished writer, but the time always seems to come, after an author's death, when somebody thinks it worth his while to write a letter to the *Times Literary Supplement** announcing the preparation of a biography* and asking to see any letters or documents or receive any anecdotes* from friends of the dead man. Most of the biographies, of course, never appear – one wonders whether the whole thing may not be an obscure form of blackmail and whether many a potential writer of a biography or thesis* finds the means in this way to finish his education at Kansas or Nottingham*. Jerome, however, as a chartered accountant*, lived far from the literary world. He did not realize how small the menace* really was, or that the danger period for someone of his father's obscurity* had long passed. Sometimes he rehearsed the method of recounting his father's death so as to reduce the comic element to its smallest dimensions – it would be of no use to refuse information, for in that case the biographer would undoubtedly visit his aunt who was living to a great old age with no sign of flagging*.

It seemed to Jerome that there were two possible methods – the first led gently up to the accident, so that by the time it was described the listener was so well prepared that the death came really as an anti-climax*. The chief danger of laughter in such a story was always surprise. When he rehearsed this method Jerome began boringly enough.

'You know Naples and those high tenement* buildings? Somebody once told me that the Neapolitan always feels at home in New York just as the man from Turin feels at home in London because the river runs in much the same way in both cities. Where was I? Oh, yes. Naples, of course. You'd be surprised in the poorer quarters what things they keep on the balconies of those sky-scraping tenements – not washing, you know, or bedding, but things like livestock*, chickens or even pigs. Of course the pigs get no exercise whatever and fatten all the quicker.' He could imagine how his hearer's eyes would have glazed* by this time. 'I've no idea, have you, how heavy a pig can be, but these old buildings are all badly in need of repair. A balcony on the fifth floor gave way under one of those pigs. It struck the third floor balcony on its way down and sort of ricochetted* into the street. My father was on the way to the Hydrographic Museum when the pig hit him. Coming from that height and that angle it broke his neck.' This was really a masterly attempt to make an intrinsically* interesting subject boring.

The other method Jerome rehearsed had the virtue of brevity*.

'My father was killed by a pig.'

'Really? In India?'

'No, in Italy.'

'How interesting. I never realized there was pig-sticking* in Italy. Was your father keen on polo*?'

In course of time, neither too early nor too late, rather as though, in his capacity as a chartered accountant, Jerome had studied the statistics and taken the average*, he became engaged to be married: to a pleasant fresh-faced girl of twenty-five whose father was a doctor in Pinner*. Her name was Sally, her favourite author was still Hugh Walpole*, and she had adored babies ever since she had been given a doll at the age of five which moved its eyes and made water. Their relationship was contented rather than exciting, as became* the love-affair of a chartered accountant; it would never have done if it had interfered with the figures.

One thought worried Jerome, however. Now that within a year he might himself become a father, his love for the dead man increased; he realized what affection had gone into the picture-postcards. He felt a longing to protect his memory, and uncertain whether this quiet love of his would survive if Sally were so insensitive as to laugh when she heard the story of his father's death. Inevitably she would hear it when Jerome brought her to dinner with his aunt. Several times he tried to tell her himself, as she was naturally anxious to know all she could that concerned him.

'You were very small when your father died?'

'Just nine.'

'Poor little boy,' she said.

'I was at school. They broke the news to me.'

'Did you take it very hard?'

'I can't remember.'

'You never told me how it happened.'

'It was very sudden. A street accident.'

'You'll never drive fast, will you, Jemmy?' (She had begun to call him 'Jemmy'.) It was too late then to try the second method – the one he thought of as the pig-sticking one.

They were going to marry quietly in a registry-office* and have their honeymoon at Torquay*. He avoided taking her to see his aunt until a week before the wedding, but then the night came, and he could not have told himself whether his apprehension was more for his father's memory or the security of his own love.

The moment came all too soon. 'Is that Jemmy's father?' Sally asked, picking up the portrait of the man with the umbrella.

'Yes, dear. How did you guess?'

'He has Jemmy's eyes and brow, hasn't he?'

'Has Jerome lent you his books?'

'No.'

'I will give you a set for your wedding. He wrote so tenderly about his travels. My own favourite is *Nooks and Crannies**. He would have had a great future. It made that shocking accident all the worse.'

'Yes?'

Jerome longed to leave the room and not see that loved face crinkle* with irresistible* amusement.

'I had so many letters from his readers after the pig fell on him.' She had never been so abrupt before.

And then the miracle* happened. Sally did not laugh. Sally sat with open eyes of horror while his aunt told her the story, and at the end, 'How horrible,' Sally said. 'It makes you think, doesn't it? Happening like that. Out of a clear sky.'

Jerome's heart sang with joy. It was as though she had appeased* his fear for ever. In the taxi going home he kissed her with more passion than he had ever shown and she returned it. There were babies in her pale blue pupils*, babies that rolled their eyes and made water.

'A week today,' Jerome said, and she squeezed his hand. 'Penny for your thoughts*, my darling.'

'I was wondering,' Sally said, 'what happened to the poor pig?'

'They almost certainly had it for dinner,' Jerome said happily and kissed the dear child* again.

Glossary

The meanings given below are those which the words and phrases have as they occur in the story.

Page
67 *housemaster*: teacher in charge of a house (a building where a group of pupils in a private school live).
proprietor: owner.
preparatory school: a private school (here only for boys) for children aged about 7–13.
Marlborough or Rugby: leading English private schools.
appearance of perplexity and apprehension: he looked confused and worried.
odd: strange.
trigonometry: a branch of mathematics.
widowed: his wife had died.
ran guns: brought guns into a country unlawfully.
a hail: a large number.

68 *as a last resort*: after all other alternatives had failed.
inexplicable: something that cannot be explained.
convulsion: sudden movement.
quarters: area where people live.
balconies: platforms built out from the wall of a building.
callousness: lack of feeling.

69 *brooded*: thought deeply for a long time.
public school (Br.E.): a better-known private school.
disclosure: telling of a secret.
snapshot: a casually taken photograph.
Rambles: walks for enjoyment.
Balearics: the islands of Ibiza, Majorca and Minorca off the east coast of Spain.
commiseration: pity and sympathy.
rambling discourse: disordered talk.
water-filter: an object that cleans water so it can be drunk.
Hydrographic: to do with the sea.

70 *Times Literary Supplement*: a British literary magazine.
biography: written account of a person's life.
anecdotes: short interesting stories.

thesis: long piece of writing needed to get a higher university degree.

Kansas or Nottingham: universities in the United States and England. The passage means that perhaps some students finance their university education from the money they get from writers who pay the students money so they will not make public embarrassing stories about the author's lives (blackmail).

chartered accountant: a fully qualified accountant.

menace: danger.

obscurity: being unknown.

flagging: becoming weaker or less active.

anti-climax: an unexciting ending when something interesting had been expected.

tenement: large building divided into flats.

livestock: animals usually kept on a farm.

glazed: looked lifeless because bored.

ricochetted: bounced off at a different angle.

71 *intrinsically*: in itself.

brevity: being short.

pig-sticking: hunting wild pigs with spears (long sticks with sharp pointed ends).

polo: a ball game played on horseback (usually an upper-class sport).

taken the average: estimated the average age when people got married.

Pinner: a suburb in north-west London.

Hugh Walpole: novelist (1884–1941). A popular writer of romantic stories, often about upper-middle class life.

as became: as was suitable for.

72 *registry-office*: office where marriages can take place.

Torquay: a seaside town in Devon, south-west England.

Nooks and Crannies: hidden and little-known places.

crinkle: become lined when she laughed.

irresistible: helpless, unable to stop herself.

miracle: wonderful and surprising thing.

appeased: made calm.

pupils: the black part of the eyes.

Penny for your thoughts: a way of asking someone what they are thinking about.
the dear child: Sally.

Questions

1. What is Jerome's aunt like?

   (a) What does Greene say about the aunt's sense of humour? (p. 69)

   (b) Greene says that the aunt's way of telling a story is 'rambling'. (p. 69) What does this mean?

   (c) The aunt is 'living to a great old age with no sign of flagging'. (p. 70) What does this mean?

   (d) What details show that the aunt admires Jerome's father's books? (p. 72)

2. How does Greene show that there is a closeness and similarity between Jerome and his father?

   (a) How does Jerome think about his father when he is eight or nine (p. 67), sixteen (p. 69) and just before he marries (p. 71)?

   (b) Jerome's aunt says the father was 'a careful man'. (p. 69) What details show that this is true? (p. 69)

   (c) What do the titles of the father's books tell us about the books themselves and the sort of person he was? (pp. 69, 72)

   (d) Consider Jerome's job (p. 70), the type of girl he is going to marry (p. 71), the planned wedding (p. 72) and the honeymoon (p. 72). How do they show that Jerome and his father are similar?

3. What part does repetition play in the humour of the story?

   (a) Mr Wordsworth (p. 68), Jerome's aunt (pp. 69, 72) and Jerome himself (pp. 70–2) all give accounts of the 'shocking accident'. Describe the way in which each tells the story. (Jerome and his aunt tell the story more than once.)

   (b) 'There were babies in her pale blue pupils, babies that rolled their eyes and made water'. (p. 72) What does this mean here? Where has there been a similar reference to babies earlier? What is the difference between the two?

(c) Sally asks 'what happened to the poor pig?' (p. 72) Where has this been said before? Why is Jerome so happy to hear Sally say this?

Language Activities

Style and Variation

Part of the humour of 'A Shocking Accident' comes from the way the main event is told in different ways by different people throughout the story.

1. Below is a 'cut-up' version of Jerome's aunt's way of telling the shocking accident. Put the sentences into the correct order.

(a) He always carried a water-filter with him.

(b) I suppose one has to regard Italy as civilized.

(c) A shocking accident.

(d) My brother always said that his filter paid for his dinner wine.

(e) I can't think how such things can be allowed in a civilized country.

(f) It was far less expensive, you know, than buying all those bottles of mineral water.

(g) You can see from that what a careful man he was, but who could have expected when he was walking along the Via Dottore Manuele Panucci on his way to the Hydrographic Museum that a pig would fall on him?

(h) One is prepared for all kinds of things abroad, of course, and my brother was a great traveller.

Jerome's aunt is boring because she gives too many details that are not really essential. Which sentences could be left out?

Would the listener be prepared for the fact that the accident involves a pig? What effect would that information have on the listener when it is finally given?

2. Below is a 'cut-up' version of Jerome's way of telling the same story when he wants to sound boring.
   Put the sentences into the correct order.

   (a) You'd be surprised in the poorer quarters what things they keep on the balconies in those sky-scraping tenements – not washing, you know, or bedding, but things like livestock, chickens and even pigs.

   (b) You know Naples and those high tenement buildings?

   (c) I've no idea, have you, how heavy a pig can be, but these old buildings are all badly in need of repair.

   (d) It struck the third floor balcony on its ways down and sort of ricochetted into the street.

   (e) Where was I? Oh, yes. Naples, of course.

   (f) Of course the pigs get no exercise whatever and fatten all the quicker.

   (g) Coming from that height and that angle it broke his neck.

   (h) Somebody once told me that the Neapolitan always feels at home in New York just as the man from Turin feels at home in London because the river runs in much the same way in both cities.

   (i) My father was on the way to the Hydrographic Museum when the pig hit him.

   (j) A balcony on the fifth floor gave way under one of those pigs.

Which sentences are not really essential to the story and could be left out?

How is the listener prepared for the information that Jerome's father was killed by a pig? Why does Jerome wish to prepare his listeners?

Idea for Writing

Write the letter that the hospital in Naples wrote to Jerome's aunt breaking the news that Jerome's father had been killed by a pig. Begin, 'Dear Miss Carruthers, It is with deep regret that we have to inform you of . . .'

Muriel Spark

Muriel Spark was born in 1918 and grew up in Edinburgh. Her first success as a novelist came in 1957 with *The Comforters*, and she reached an even wider readership later with *The Ballad of Peckham Rye* (1960) and *The Prime of Miss Jean Brodie* (1961), which also appeared as a play and a film. Muriel Spark has in addition published poetry and several collections of short stories. 'You Should Have Seen the Mess', taken from *The Go-Away Bird and Other Stories* (1958), is typical of her amusing and original style.

The story

Lorna is seventeen years old and comes from a working class family. For her, cleanliness is the most important thing in the world. Unfortunately, other people do not always see things the way she does. The story is told through Lorna's eyes and in her own words.

You Should Have Seen the Mess*

I AM now more than glad that I did not pass into the grammar school* five years ago, although it was a disappointment at the time. I was always good at English, but not so good at the other subjects!!

I am glad that I went to the secondary modern school*, because it was only constructed the year before. Therefore, it was much more hygienic than the grammar school. The secondary modern was light and airy, and the walls were painted with a bright, washable gloss. One day, I was sent over to the grammar school, with a note for one of the teachers, and you should have seen the mess! The corridors were dusty, and I saw dust on the window ledges, which were chipped. I saw into one of the classrooms. It was very untidy in there.

I am also glad that I did not go to the grammar school, because of what it does to one's habits. This may appear to be a strange remark, at first sight. It is a good thing to have an education behind you, and I do not believe in ignorance, but I have had certain experiences, with educated people, since going out into the world.

I am seventeen years of age, and left school two years ago last month. I had my A certificate for typing, so got my first job, as a junior, in a solicitor's* office. Mum was pleased at this, and Dad said it was a first-class start, as it was an old-established firm. I must say that when I went for the interview, I was surprised at the windows, and the stairs up to the offices were also far from clean. There was a little waiting-room, where some of the elements were missing from the gas fire, and the carpet on the floor was worn. However, Mr Heygate's office, into which I was shown for the interview, was better. The furniture was old, but it was polished, and there was a good carpet, I will say. The glass of the bookcase was very clean.

I was to start on the Monday, so along I went. They took me to the general office, where there were two senior shorthand-typists, and a clerk, Mr Gresham, who was far from smart in appearance. You should have seen the mess!! There was no floor covering whatsoever, and so dusty everywhere. There were shelves all round the room, with old box files* on them. The box files were falling to pieces, and all the old papers inside them were crumpled. The worst shock of all was the tea-cups. It was my duty to make tea, mornings and after-noons. Miss Bewlay showed me where everything was kept. It was kept in an old orange box, and the cups were all cracked. There were not enough saucers to go round, etc. I will not go into the facilities*, but they were also far from hygienic. After three days, I told Mum, and she was upset, most of all about the cracked cups. We never keep a cracked cup, but throw it out, because those cracks can harbour germs*. So Mum gave me my own cup to take to the office.

Then at the end of the week, when I got my salary, Mr Heygate said. 'Well, Lorna, what are you going to do with your first pay?' I did not like him saying this, and I nearly passed a comment, but I said, 'I don't know.' He said, 'What do you do in the evenings, Lorna? Do you watch Telly?' I did take this as an insult, because we call it TV, and his remark made me out to be uneducated. I just stood, and did not answer, and he looked surprised. Next day, Saturday, I told Mum and Dad about the facilities, and we decided I should not go back to that job. Also, the desks in the general office were rickety*. Dad was indignant*, because Mr Heygate's concern was flourishing*, and he had letters after his name.

Everyone admires our flat, because Mum keeps it spotless, and Dad keeps doing things to it. He has done it up all over, and got permission from the Council* to remodernize the kitchen. I well recall the Health Visitor*, remarking to Mum, 'You could eat off your floor, Mrs Merrifield.' It is true that you could eat your lunch off Mum's floors, and any hour of the day or night you will find every corner spick and span*.

Next, I was sent by the agency* to a publisher's for an interview, because of being good at English. One look was enough!! My next interview was a success, and I am still at Low's Chemical Co. It is a modern block, with a quarter of an hour rest period, morning and afternoon. Mr Marwood is very smart in appearance. He is well spoken, although he has not got a university education behind him. There is special lighting over the desks, and the typewriters are the latest models.

So I am happy at Low's. But I have met other people, of an educated type, in the past year, and it has opened my eyes. It so happened that I had to go to the doctor's house, to fetch a prescription* for my young brother, Trevor, when the epidemic* was on. I rang the bell, and Mrs Darby came to the door. She was small, with fair hair, but too long, and a green maternity dress*. But she was very nice to me. I had to wait in their living-room, and you should have seen the state it was in! There were broken toys on the carpet, and the ash trays were full up. There were contemporary pictures on the walls, but the furniture was not contemporary, but old-fashioned, with covers which were past standing up to another wash*, I should say. To cut a long story short, Dr Darby and Mrs Darby have always been very kind to me, and they meant everything for the best. Dr Darby is also short and fair, and they have three children, a girl and a boy, and now a baby boy.

When I went that day for the prescription, Dr Darby said to me, 'You look pale, Lorna. It's the London atmosphere. Come on a picnic with us, in the car, on Saturday.' After that I went with the Darbys more and more. I liked them, but I did not like the mess, and it was a surprise. But I also kept in with them* for the opportunity of meeting people, and Mum and Dad were pleased that I had made nice friends. So I did not say anything about the cracked lino*, and the paintwork all chipped. The children's clothes were very shabby* for a doctor, and she changed them out of their school clothes when they came home from school, into those worn-out garments. Mum always kept us spotless to go out to play, and I do not like to say it, but those Darby children frequently looked like the Leary family, which the Council evicted* from our block, as they were far from houseproud.

One day, when I was there, Mavis (as I called Mrs Darby by then) put her head out of the window, and shouted to the boy, 'John, stop peeing* over the cabbages at once. Pee on the lawn.' I did not know which way to look. Mum would never say a word like that from the window, and I know for a fact that Trevor would never pass water outside, not even bathing in the sea.

I went there usually at the week-ends, but sometimes on week-days, after supper. They had an idea to make a match for me* with a chemist's assistant, whom they had taken up too. He was an orphan, and I do not say there was anything wrong with that. But he was not accustomed to those little extras* that I was. He was a good-looking boy, I will say that. So I went once to a dance, and twice to films with him. To look at, he was quite clean in appearance. But there was only hot water at the week-end at his place, and he said that a bath once a week was sufficient. Jim (as I called Dr Darby by then) said it was sufficient also, and surprised me. He did not have much money, and I do not hold that against him. But there was no hurry for me, and I could wait for a man in a better position, so that I would not miss those little extras. So he started going out with a girl from the coffee bar, and did not come to the Darbys very much then.

There were plenty of boys at the office, but I will say this for the Darbys, they had lots of friends coming and going, and they had interesting conversation, although sometimes it gave me a surprise, and I did not know where to look. And sometimes they had people who were very down and out*, although there is no need to be. But most of the guests were different, so it made a comparison with the boys at the office, who were not so educated in their conversation.

Now it was near the time for Mavis to have her baby, and I was to come in at the week-end, to keep an eye on the children, while the help* had her day off. Mavis did not go away to have her baby, but would have it at home, in their double bed, as they did not have twin beds*, although he was a doctor. A girl I knew, in our block, was engaged, but was let down*, and even she had her baby in the labour ward*. I was sure the bedroom was not hygienic for having a baby, but I did not mention it.

One day, after the baby boy came along, they took me in the car to the country, to see Jim's mother. The baby was put in a carry-cot* at the back of the car. He began to cry, and without a word of a lie, Jim said to him over his shoulder, 'Oh shut your gob*, you little bastard*'. I did not know what to do, and Mavis was smoking a cigarette. Dad would not dream of saying such a thing to Trevor or I. When we arrived at Jim's mother's place, Jim said, 'It's a fourteenth-century cottage, Lorna.' I could well believe it. It was very cracked and old, and it made one wonder how Jim could let his old mother live in this tumble-down* cottage, as he was so good to everyone else. So Mavis knocked at the door, and the old lady came. There was not much anyone could do to the inside. Mavis said, 'Isn't it charming, Lorna?' If that was a joke, it was going too far. I said to the old Mrs Darby, 'Are you going to be re-housed*?' but she did not understand this, and I explained how you have to apply to the Council, and keep at them*. But it was funny that the Council had not done something already, when they go round condemning*. Then old Mrs Darby said, 'My dear, I shall be re-housed in the Grave.' I did not know where to look.

There was a carpet hanging on the wall, which I think was there to hide a damp spot. She had a good TV set, I will say that. But some of the walls were bare brick, and the facilities were outside, through the garden. The furniture was far from new.

One Saturday afternoon, as I happened to go to the Darbys, they were just going off to a film and they took me too. It was the Curzon, and afterwards we went to a flat in Curzon Street. It was a very clean block, I will say that, and there were good carpets at the entrance. The couple there had contemporary furniture, and they also spoke about music. It was a nice place, but there was no Welfare Centre* to the flats, where people could go for social intercourse, advice, and guidance. But they were well-spoken, and I met Willy Morley, who was an artist. Willy sat beside me, and we had a drink. He was young, dark, with a dark shirt, so one could not see right away if he was clean. Soon after this, Jim said to me, 'Willy wants to paint you, Lorna. But you'd better ask your Mum.' Mum said it was all right if he was a friend of the Darbys.

I can honestly say that Willy's place was the most

unhygienic place I have seen in my life. He said I had an unusual type of beauty, which he must capture. This was when we came back to his place from the restaurant. The light was very dim, but I could see the bed had not been made, and the sheets were far from clean. He said he must paint me, but I told Mavis I did not like to go back there. 'Don't you like Willy?' she asked. I could not deny that I liked Willy, in a way. There was something about him, I will say that. Mavis said, 'I hope he hasn't been making a pass* at you, Lorna.' I said he had not done so, which was almost true, because he did not attempt to go to the full extent*. It was always unhygienic when I went to Willy's place, and I told him so once, but he said, 'Lorna, you are a joy.' He had a nice way, and he took me out in his car, which was a good one, but dirty inside, like his place. Jim said one day, 'He has pots of money, Lorna,' and Mavis said, 'You might make a man of him, as he is keen on you.' They always said Willy came from a good family.

But I saw that one could not do anything with him. He would not change his shirt very often, or get clothes, but he went round like a tramp*, lending people money, as I have seen with my own eyes. His place was in a terrible mess, with the empty bottles, and laundry in the corner. He gave me several gifts over the period, which I took as he would have only given them away; but he never tried to go to the full extent. He never painted my portrait, as he was painting fruit on a table all that time, and they said his pictures were marvellous, and thought Willy and I were getting married.

One night, when I went home, I was upset as usual, after Willy's place. Mum and Dad had gone to bed, and I looked round our kitchen which is done* in primrose and white. Then I went into the living-room, where Dad has done one wall in a patterned paper, deep rose and white, and the other walls pale rose, with white woodwork. The suite* is new, and Mum keeps everything beautiful. So it came to me, all of a sudden, what a fool I was, going with Willy. I agree to equality, but as to me marrying Willy, as I said to Mavis, when I recall his place, and the good carpet gone greasy, not to mention the paint oozing out of the tubes, I think it would break my heart to sink so low.

Glossary

The meanings given below are those which the words and phrases have as they occur in the story.

Page
79   *Mess*: untidiness, dirtiness.

grammar school: type of British school that provides a more academic education to children over the age of 11.

secondary modern school: school that gives a more general and technical education than a grammar school.

solicitor: a type of lawyer.

80   *box files*: boxes which keep papers together and in order.

facilities: she is referring here to the toilet (lavatory).

can harbour germs: small living things that cause disease can live there.

rickety: unsteady, likely to break.

indignant: angry.

concern was flourishing: his business was doing well.

Council: local government.

Health Visitor: medical worker who visits families.

spick and span: clean and tidy.

agency: organization that finds jobs for people.

81   *prescription*: a written order for medicine given to a patient by a doctor.

epidemic: rapidly spreading, widespread occurrence of a certain disease.

maternity dress: dress worn by a woman who is going to have a baby.

past standing up to another wash: could not take another wash as they were too old.

kept in with them: stayed friends with them.

lino: hard shiny floor covering.

shabby: old and poor looking.

evicted: made them leave their home.

peeing: (coll.): passing water, urinating.

82   *make a match for me*: plan for me to marry.

those little extras: her family could afford more things than he could.

down and out: people with no money or work.

the help: woman who is paid to do the housework.

twin beds: a pair of single beds.

let down: the boy she was engaged to left her when she was pregnant.

labour ward: hospital room where women have their babies.

83 *carry-cot*: a type of box in which a baby can be carried.

gob (sl.): an impolite word for mouth.

bastard (sl.): an insulting swear-word.

tumble-down: old, likely to fall down.

re-housed: put in a newer and better home.

keep at them: keep asking them.

condemning: saying old houses must be pulled down.

Welfare Centre: office to help with the social and housing needs of the people from a certain area (usually a poorer area).

84 *making a pass*: for example, trying to kiss.

to go to the full extent: to have sex with her.

tramp: person with no money or work who travels around asking people for money.

done: decorated.

suite: a set of furniture.

Questions

1. Lorna has very clear ideas about what she approves or does not approve of. List the following under the heading either FOR (i.e. the things Lorna approves of) or AGAINST (the things she doesn't approve of). Then decide why she is for or against them.

   (a) a good education
   (b) the solicitor's office
   (c) Mr Heygate
   (d) the publisher's
   (e) Low's Chemical Co.
   (f) Dr and Mrs Darby

(g) the Leary family
(h) the chemist's assistant
(i) old Mrs Darby's cottage
(j) Willy Morley

2. How does the story deal with class differences in English society?

   (a) Why is Lorna insulted because Mr Heygate uses the word 'Telly' rather than 'TV'? Why is he surprised at Lorna's reaction? (p. 80)

   (b) Lorna is shocked at some of the Darbys' language. Why? (pp. 81–83)

   (c) Why does Lorna want to 'keep in with' the Darbys? (p. 81)

   (d) Why does Lorna reject the chemist's assistant? (p. 82)

   (e) Where has she got her ideas of cleanliness from? (pp. 80, 84)

   (f) Lorna says she does not like what the grammar school 'does to one's habits'. (p. 79) What does she mean?

   (g) Why does Muriel Spark end her story with the word 'low'?

Language Activities

Euphemisms

When someone says 'She fell asleep', meaning 'She died', he is using a euphemism. Euphemism is the use of an indirect but pleasanter way of saying something which, if said straight out, might sound harsh or disagreeable.

Part of the humorous effect of 'You Should Have Seen the Mess' is that Lorna is easily shocked and often uses euphemisms to avoid saying something she thinks is unpleasant. What does she mean in the following?

(a) the offices were also far from clean. (p. 79)

(b) Mr Gresham, who was far from smart in appearance. (p. 80)

(c) I will not go into the facilities, but they were also far from hygienic. (p. 80)

(d) A girl I knew . . . was engaged, but was let down. (p. 82)

Clichés

A cliché is an expression that is used so often that it has lost any special force it once had. An example is Lorna's repeated use of the expression 'far from'. Expressing herself as she does by means of many clichés, Lorna shows how limited her thinking really is.

Rephrase in your own words these expressions that Lorna frequently uses:

(a) I will say that.

(b) You should have seen the mess!!

(c) I did not know where to look.

Lorna's Thoughts

The links that Lorna makes between one thought and the next are rather unusual and reveal a lot about her.

Explain the following paying particular attention to the linking words that are underlined:

(a) She was small, with fair hair, but too long, and a green maternity dress. <u>But</u> she was very nice to me. (p. 81)

(b) they did not have twin beds, <u>although</u> he was a doctor. (p. 82)

(c) A girl I knew . . . was engaged, but was let down, and <u>even she</u> had her baby in the labour ward. (p. 82)

(d) He gave me several gifts . . . <u>but</u> he never tried to go to the full extent. (p. 84)

Ideas for Writing

1. Lorna decides to leave Low's Chemical Co. and applies for a better job as a typist in an international company. Write her letter of application giving details of her qualifications, interests and future plans. Begin, 'Dear Sir, I would like to

apply for the job as a typist with your company . . .'

2. Imagine that Lorna decides to marry Willy and that the final paragraph begins 'One night, when I went home, I thought to myself "Why not? Why not marry Willy!" ' Complete the story.

* * * * * *

1. Which of these two stories do you prefer? What are some of the reasons for your choice?

2. What decisions are made in these two stories? Did Jerome and Lorna both make the right decision?

Crime

Roald Dahl

Roald Dahl was born in 1916 in South Wales, though his parents were Norwegian. During the Second World War he was a fighter pilot and his first collection of short stories *Over to You* (1942) is about the tensions of war-time flying. Since then Roald Dahl has become known as one of the world's most popular writers – children finding his children's books as fascinating as grown-ups find his more adult short stories. Dahl's secret is that he can be both shocking and witty at the same time, and few can match his mastery of the unexpected ending. A good collection of his short stories is *The Best of Roald Dahl* (1983). 'Lamb to the Slaughter' was first published in *Someone Like You* (1954).

The story

Mary Maloney adores her husband, and every evening she eagerly awaits his return from work. Tonight, however, things will be a little different . . .

Lamb to the Slaughter*

T HE room was warm and clean, the curtains drawn, the two table lamps alight – hers and the one by the empty chair opposite. On the sideboard behind her, two tall glasses, soda water, whisky. Fresh ice cubes in the Thermos bucket*.

Mary Maloney* was waiting for her husband to come home from work.

Now and again she would glance up at the clock, but without anxiety, merely to please herself with the thought that each minute gone by made it nearer the time when he would come. There was a slow smiling air about her, and about everything she did. The drop of the head as she bent over her sewing was curiously tranquil. Her skin – for this was her sixth month with child* – had acquired a wonderful translucent* quality, the mouth was soft, and the eyes, with their new placid look, seemed larger, darker than before.

When the clock said ten minutes to five, she began to listen, and a few moments later, punctually as always, she heard the tyres on the gravel outside, and the car door slamming, the footsteps passing the window, the key turning in the lock. She laid aside her sewing, stood up, and went forward to kiss him as he came in.

'Hullo, darling,' she said.

'Hullo,' he answered.

She took his coat and hung it in the closet*. Then she walked over and made the drinks, a strongish one for him, a weak one for herself; and soon she was back again in her chair with the sewing, and he in the other, opposite, holding the tall glass with both his hands, rocking it so the ice cubes tinkled against the side.

For her, this was always a blissful time of day. She knew he didn't want to speak much until the first drink was finished, and she, on her side, was content to sit quietly, enjoying his company after the long hours alone in the house. She loved to luxuriate in the presence of this man, and to feel – almost as a sunbather feels the sun – that warm male glow that came out of him to her when they were alone together. She loved him for the way he sat loosely in a chair, for the way he came in a door, or moved slowly across the room with long strides*. She loved the intent, far look in his eyes when they rested on her, the funny shape of the mouth, and especially the way he remained silent about his tiredness, sitting still with himself until the whisky had taken some of it away.

'Tired, darling?'

'Yes,' he said. 'I'm tired.' And as he spoke, he did an unusual thing. He lifted his glass and drained it in one swallow although there was still half of it, at least half of it, left. She wasn't really watching him but she knew what he had done because she heard the ice cubes falling back against the bottom of the empty glass when he lowered his arm. He paused a moment, leaning forward in the chair, then he got up and went slowly over to fetch himself another.

'I'll get it!' she cried, jumping up.

'Sit down,' he said.

When he came back, she noticed that the new drink was dark amber with the quantity of whisky in it.

'Darling, shall I get your slippers?'

'No.'

She watched him as he began to sip the dark yellow drink, and she could see little oily swirls* in the liquid because it was so strong.

'I think it's a shame,' she said, 'that when a policeman gets to be as senior as you, they keep him walking about on his feet all day long.'

He didn't answer, so she bent her head again and went on with her sewing; but each time he lifted the drink to his lips, she heard the ice cubes clinking against the side of the glass.

'Darling,' she said. 'Would you like me to get you some cheese? I haven't made any supper because it's Thursday.'

'No.' he said.

'If you're too tired to eat out,' she went on, 'it's still not too late. There's plenty of meat and stuff in the freezer, and you can have it right here and not even move out of the chair.'

Her eyes waited on him for an answer, a smile, a little

nod, but he made no sign.

'Anyway,' she went on, 'I'll get you some cheese and crackers* first.'

'I don't want it,' he said.

She moved uneasily in her chair, the large eyes still watching his face. 'But you *must* have supper. I can easily do it here. I'd like to do it. We can have lamb chops. Or pork. Anything you want. Everything's in the freezer.'

'Forget it,' he said.

'But, darling, you *must* eat! I'll fix it anyway, and then you can have it or not, as you like.'

She stood up and placed her sewing on the table by the lamp.

'Sit down,' he said. 'Just for a minute, sit down.'

It wasn't till then that she began to get frightened.

'Go on,' he said. 'Sit down.'

She lowered herself back slowly into the chair, watching him all the time with those large, bewildered eyes. He had finished the second drink and was staring down into the glass, frowning.

'Listen,' he said. 'I've got something to tell you.'

'What is it, darling? What's the matter?'

He had become absolutely motionless, and he kept his head down so that the light from the lamp beside him fell across the upper part of his face, leaving the chin and mouth in shadow. She noticed there was a little muscle moving near the corner of his left eye.

'This is going to be a bit of a shock to you, I'm afraid,' he said. 'But I've thought about it a good deal and I've decided the only thing to do is tell you right away. I hope you won't blame me too much.'

And he told her. It didn't take long, four or five minutes at most, and she sat very still through it all, watching him with a kind of dazed horror as he went further and further away from her with each word.

'So there it is,' he added. 'And I know it's kind of a bad time to be telling you, but there simply wasn't any other way. Of course I'll give you money and see you're looked after. But there needn't really be any fuss. I hope not anyway. It wouldn't be very good for my job.'

Her first instinct was not to believe any of it, to reject it all. It occurred to her that perhaps he hadn't even spoken, that she herself had imagined the whole thing. Maybe, if she went about her business and acted as though she hadn't been listening, then later, when she sort of woke up again, she might find none of it had ever happened.

'I'll get the supper,' she managed to whisper, and this time he didn't stop her.

When she walked across the room she couldn't feel her feet touching the floor. She couldn't feel anything at all – except a slight nausea* and a desire to vomit*. Everything was automatic now – down the stairs to the cellar, the light switch, the deep freeze, the hand inside the cabinet taking hold of the first object it met. She lifted it out, and looked at it. It was wrapped in paper, so she took off the paper and looked at it again.

A leg of lamb.

All right then, they would have lamb for supper. She carried it upstairs, holding the thin bone-end of it with both her hands, and as she went through the living-room, she saw him standing over by the window with his back to her, and she stopped.

'For God's sake,' he said, hearing her, but not turning round. 'Don't make supper for me. I'm going out.'

At that point, Mary Maloney simply walked up behind him and without any pause she swung the big frozen leg of lamb high in the air and brought it down as hard as she could on the back of his head.

She might just as well have hit him with a steel club*.

She stepped back a pace, waiting, and the funny thing was that he remained standing there for at least four or five seconds, gently swaying*. Then he crashed to the carpet.

The violence of the crash, the noise, the small table overturning, helped bring her out of the shock. She came out slowly, feeling cold and surprised, and she stood for a while blinking at the body, still holding the ridiculous piece of meat tight with both hands.

All right, she told herself. So I've killed him.

It was extraordinary, now, how clear her mind became all of

a sudden. She began thinking very fast. As the wife of a detective, she knew quite well what the penalty would be. That was fine. It made no difference to her. In fact, it would be a relief. On the other hand, what about the child? What were the laws about murderers with unborn children? Did they kill them both – mother and child? Or did they wait until the tenth month? What did they do?

Mary Maloney didn't know. And she certainly wasn't prepared to take a chance.

She carried the meat into the kitchen, placed it in a pan, turned the oven on high, and shoved it inside. Then she washed her hands and ran upstairs to the bedroom. She sat down before the mirror, tidied her face, touched up her lips and face. She tried a smile. It came out rather peculiar. She tried again.

'Hullo Sam,' she said brightly, aloud.

The voice sounded peculiar too.

'I want some potatoes please, Sam. Yes, and I think a can of peas.'

That was better. Both the smile and the voice were coming out better now. She rehearsed it several times more. Then she ran downstairs, took her coat, went out the back door, down the garden, into the street.

It wasn't six o'clock yet and the lights were still on in the grocery shop.

'Hullo Sam.' she said brightly, smiling at the man behind the counter.

'Why, good evening, Mrs Maloney. How're *you*?'

'I want some potatoes please, Sam. Yes, and I think a can of peas.'

The man turned and reached up behind him on the shelf for the peas.

'Patrick's decided he's tired and doesn't want to eat out tonight,' she told him. 'We usually go out Thursdays, you know, and now he's caught me without any vegetables in the house.'

'Then how about meat, Mrs Maloney?'

'No, I've got meat, thanks. I got a nice leg of lamb, from the freezer.'

'Oh.'

'I don't much like cooking it frozen, Sam, but I'm taking a chance on it this time. You think it'll be all right?'

'Personally,' the grocer said, 'I don't believe it makes any difference. You want these Idaho potatoes*?'

'Oh yes, that'll be fine. Two of those.'

'Anything else?' The grocer cocked his head on one side, looking at her pleasantly. 'How about afterwards? What you going to give him for afterwards?'

'Well – what would you suggest, Sam?'

The man glanced around his shop. 'How about a nice big slice of cheesecake*? I know he likes that.'

'Perfect,' she said. 'He loves it.'

And when it was all wrapped and she had paid, she put on her brightest smile and said. 'Thank you, Sam. Good night.'

'Good night, Mrs Maloney. And thank *you*.'

And now, she told herself as she hurried back, all she was doing now, she was returning home to her husband and he was waiting for his supper; and she must cook it good, and make it as tasty as possible because the poor man was tired; and if, when she entered the house, she happened to find anything unusual, or tragic, or terrible, then naturally it would be a shock and she'd become frantic with grief and horror. Mind you, she wasn't *expecting* to find anything. She was just going home with the vegetables. Mrs Patrick Maloney going home with the vegetables on Thursday evening to cook supper for her husband.

That's the way, she told herself. Do everything right and natural. Keep things absolutely natural and there'll be no need for any acting at all.

Therefore, when she entered the kitchen by the back door, she was humming a little tune to herself and smiling.

'Patrick!' she called. 'How are you, darling?'

She put the parcel down on the table and went through into the living-room; and when she saw him lying there on the floor with his legs doubled up and one arm twisted back underneath his body, it really was rather a shock. All the old love and longing for him welled up* inside her, and she ran over to him, knelt down beside him, and began to cry her heart out. It was easy. No acting was necessary.

A few minutes later she got up and went to the phone. She knew the number of the police station, and when the man at the other end answered, she cried to him, 'Quick! Come quick! Patrick's dead!'

'Who's speaking?'

'Mrs Maloney. Mrs Patrick Maloney.'

'You mean Patrick Maloney's dead?'

'I think so,' she sobbed. 'He's lying on the floor and I think he's dead.'

'Be right over,' the man said.

The car came very quickly, and when she opened the front door, two policemen walked in. She knew them both – she knew nearly all the men at that precinct* – and she fell right into Jack Noonan's arms, weeping hysterically. He put her gently into a chair, then went over to join the other one, who was called O'Malley, kneeling by the body.

'Is he dead?' she cried.

'I'm afraid he is. What happened?'

Briefly, she told her story about going out to the grocer and coming back to find him on the floor. While she was talking, crying and talking, Noonan discovered a small patch of congealed* blood on the dead man's head. He showed it to O'Malley who got up at once and hurried to the phone.

Soon, other men began to come into the house. First a doctor, then two detectives, one of whom she knew by name. Later, a police photographer arrived and took pictures, and a man who knew about fingerprints. There was a great deal of whispering and muttering beside the corpse*, and the detectives kept asking her a lot of questions. But they always treated her kindly. She told her story again, this time right from the beginning, when Patrick had come in, and she was sewing, and he was tired, so tired he hadn't wanted to go out for supper. She told how she'd put the meat in the oven – 'it's there now, cooking' – and how she'd slipped out* to the grocer for vegetables, and come back to find him lying on the floor.

'Which grocer?' one of the detectives asked.

She told him, and he turned and whispered something to the other detective who immediately went outside into the street.

In fifteen minutes he was back with a page of notes, and there was more whispering, and through her sobbing she heard a few of the whispered phrases – '. . . acted quite normal . . . very cheerful . . . wanted to give him a good supper . . . peas . . . cheesecake . . . impossible that she . . .'

After a while, the photographer and the doctor departed and two other men came in and took the corpse away on a stretcher*. Then the fingerprint man went away. The two detectives remained, and so did the two policemen. They were exceptionally nice to her, and Jack Noonan asked if she wouldn't rather go somewhere else, to her sister's house perhaps, or to his own wife who would take care of her and put her up for the night.

No, she said. She didn't feel she could move even a yard at the moment. Would they mind awfully if she stayed just where she was until she felt better? She didn't feel too good at the moment, she really didn't.

Then hadn't she better lie down on the bed? Jack Noonan asked.

No, she said, she'd like to stay right where she was, in this chair. A little later perhaps, when she felt better, she would move.

So they left her there while they went about their business, searching the house. Occasionally one of the detectives asked her another question. Sometimes Jack Noonan spoke to her gently as he passed by. Her husband, he told her, had been killed by a blow on the back of the head administered with a heavy blunt* instrument, almost certainly a large piece of metal. They were looking for the weapon. The murderer may have taken it with him, but on the other hand he may've thrown it away or hidden it somewhere on the premises*.

'It's the old story,' he said, 'Get the weapon, and you've got the man.'

Later, one of the detectives came up and sat beside her. Did she know, he asked, of anything in the house that could've been used as the weapon? Would she mind having a look around to see if anything was missing – a very big spanner*, for example, or a heavy metal vase.

They didn't have any heavy metal vases, she said.

'Or a big spanner?'

She didn't think they had a big spanner. But there might be some things like that in the garage.

The search went on. She knew that there were other policemen in the garden all around the house. She could hear their footsteps on the gravel outside, and sometimes she saw the flash of a torch through a chink in the curtains. It began to get late, nearly nine she noticed by the clock on the mantel*. The four men searching the rooms seemed to be growing weary, a trifle exasperated*.

'Jack,' she said, the next time Sergeant Noonan went by. 'Would you mind giving me a drink?'

'Sure I'll give you a drink. You mean this whisky?'

'Yes, please. But just a small one. It might make me feel better.'

He handed her the glass.

'Why don't you have one yourself,' she said. 'You must be awfully tired. Please do. You've been very good to me.'

'Well,' he answered. 'It's not strictly allowed, but I might take just a drop to keep me going.'

One by one the others came in and were persuaded to take a little nip* of whisky. They stood around rather awkwardly with the drinks in their hands, uncomfortable in her presence, trying to say consoling things* to her. Sergeant Noonan wandered into the kitchen, came out quickly and said, 'Look, Mrs Maloney. You know that oven of yours is still on, and the meat still inside.'

'Oh *dear* me!' she cried. 'So it is!'

'I better turn if off for you, hadn't I?'

'Will you do that, Jack. Thank you so much.'

When the sergeant returned the second time, she looked at him with her large, dark, tearful eyes. 'Jack Noonan,' she said.

'Yes?'

'Would you do me a small favour – you and these others?'

'We can try, Mrs Maloney.'

'Well,' she said. 'Here you all are, and good friends of dear Patrick's too, and helping to catch the man who killed him. You must be terrible hungry by now because it's long past your supper time, and I know Patrick would never forgive me, God bless his soul, if I allowed you to remain in his house without offering you decent hospitality. Why don't you eat up that lamb that's in the oven? It'll be cooked just right by now.'

'Wouldn't dream of it,' Sergeant Noonan said.

'Please,' she begged. 'Please eat it. Personally I couldn't touch a thing, certainly not what's been in the house when he was here. But it's all right for you. It'd be a favour to me if you'd eat it up. Then you can go on with your work again afterwards.'

There was a good deal of hesitating among the four police-men, but they were clearly hungry, and in the end they were persuaded to go into the kitchen and help themselves. The woman stayed where she was, listening to them through the open door, and she could hear them speaking among them-selves, their voices thick and sloppy* because their mouths were full of meat.

'Have some more, Charlie?'

'No. Better not finish it.'

'She *wants* us to finish it. She said so. Be doing her a favour.'

'Okay then. Give me some more.'

'That's the hell of a big club the guy must've used to hit poor Patrick,' one of them was saying. 'The doc says his skull was smashed all to pieces just like from a sledge-hammer*.'

'That's why it ought to be easy to find.'

'Exactly what I say.'

'Whoever done it, they're not going to be carrying a thing like that around with them longer than they need.'

One of them belched*.

'Personally, I think it's right here on the premises.'

'Probably right under our very noses. What you think, Jack?'

And in the other room, Mary Maloney began to giggle.

Glossary

The meanings given below are those which the words and phrases have as they appear in the story.

Page

93   *Lamb to the Slaughter (idiom)*: to be a helpless victim. To slaughter means to kill.

Thermos bucket: a bucket that keeps ice cubes cold.

Maloney: an Irish name. The names of all the policemen given later in the story are also Irish. In many parts of the United States being a policeman is a traditional job for Irish-Americans.

her sixth month with child: her sixth month of pregnancy.

translucent: bright clearness, so the light appears to shine through the skin.

closet (Am. E.): clothes cupboard.

94   *strides*: walking steps.

swirls: curling movements.

95   *crackers*: thin, dry unsweetened biscuits.

96   *nausea*: feeling of sickness.

vomit: be sick.

steel club: heavy stick made of steel.

swaying: moving slightly in one direction and then another direction.

98   *Idaho potatoes*: Idaho is a state in the north-western United States well known for its (large) potatoes.

cheesecake: a sweet cake made from cream cheese, cream and sugar.

welled up: rose up.

99   *precinct (Am.E)*: the police station.

congealed: the blood is drying and becoming thick.

corpse: dead body.

slipped out: gone out quickly for a short time.

100   *stretcher*: a framework made with thick cloth used for carrying injured or dead people.

blunt: not sharp.

premises: the house and surrounding garden.

101   *spanner*: metal hand tool used for tightening up metal parts.

     mantel: shelf above a fireplace.

     a trifle exasperated: a little annoyed and angry.

     nip (coll.): a small drink (of spirits).

     consoling things: things that would give comfort and show sympathy.

102   *sloppy*: wet sounding.

     sledge-hammer: large heavy hammer with a long handle.

     belched: passed wind from the stomach noisily through the mouth.

Questions

1. Why do we have more sympathy for the murderer than the victim in this story?

    (a) What details at the beginning of the story show that Mrs Maloney is a loving wife? (pp. 93–5)

    (b) What is Patrick referring to when he says 'I know it's kind of a bad time to be telling you'? (p. 95)

    (c) Why does Patrick not want there to 'be any fuss' (p. 95) about what he has just told his wife?

    (d) What are Patrick's last words? (p. 96) What tone of voice might they be said in?

    (e) Pick out the words that indicate that Mary does not think before she strikes her husband. (p. 96)

    (f) What are Mary's reasons for covering up the crime? (p. 97)

2. 'I've got something to tell you' says Patrick Maloney. (p. 95) Why are we not told exactly what this 'something' is?

    (a) Write out in full what you think Patrick Maloney might have said to his wife to make her so shocked. Begin 'I hope you won't blame me too much, but . . .'

    (b) Do you think the story would be better or worse if Maloney's words were included. Give your reasons.

3. How is the reader prepared for the murder and the covering up of the crime?

  (a) Does the title give any indication that this will be a murder story?

  (b) Why does the sentence 'A leg of lamb' (p. 96) appear on a separate line?

  (c) At exactly what point does Dahl indicate that Mary will destroy the evidence of the murder weapon? Is the reader aware of this point on first reading?

  (d) Mary asks for a drink, then offers a drink to the detectives and then offers them food. Why does she do things in this order? (pp. 101–2)

Language Activities

Setting a Mood

Read the first two paragraphs (from 'The room . . .' to '. . . home from work'). Notice how the adjectives (*warm, clean, fresh*) give a feeling of warmth and comfort and suggest a pleasant atmosphere.

Now fill in the spaces below with *one* word so that the atmosphere becomes evil and threatening.

'The room was ＿＿ and ＿＿, the curtains ＿＿, the two table lamps ＿＿ – hers and the one by the ＿＿ chair opposite. On the sideboard behind her, two ＿＿ glasses, soda water, whisky. ＿＿ ice cubes in the Thermos bucket.

Mary Maloney was waiting for her husband to come home from work.'

Dahl's story involves a violent murder. Why, then, does it start with a feeling of warmth and comfort?

Point of View

In 'Lamb to the Slaughter' we see and experience things mainly from Mary's point of view. Note, for example, how we are given Patrick Maloney's words, but we can only guess what he is thinking, whereas Dahl tells us what Mary says, thinks and feels.

This is the passage after her husband has told her some shocking news:

'When she walked across the room she couldn't feel her feet touching the floor. She couldn't feel anything at all – except a slight nausea and a desire to vomit. Everything was automatic now – down the stairs to the cellar, the light switch, the deep freeze, the hand inside the cabinet taking hold of the first object it met.' (p. 96)

Imagine the scene was written like this:

'. . . Everything was automatic now – she went down the stairs to the cellar and turned on the light. She went towards the deep freeze and put her hand inside the cabinet . . .'

What is the effect created by omitting the verbs and repeating the definite article (*the* light switch, *the* deep freeze etc.)? What is the difference between 'the hand' and 'her hand'?

Ideas for Writing

1. Imagine you are Mrs Maloney and it is exactly one year since Patrick Maloney was killed. Write a letter to a good friend to say what you have been doing in the last year. Begin 'Dear Maureen, I looked at the calendar today and noticed that it was exactly a year ago today that poor Patrick was killed . . .'

2. Imagine that one of the policeman eating the lamb realizes that he is eating the murder weapon. Begin 'The weapon's probably right under our noses . . . Wait a minute! . . .' and complete the story.

James Thurber (1894-1961)

James Thurber was born in Columbus, Ohio, in the central part of the United States. He worked as a newspaperman in Columbus, Paris and New York and then joined the staff of the American magazine, *The New Yorker*. Over the years *The New Yorker* has become associated with good literary style and high quality writing; many of Thurber's now famous short stories, including 'The Catbird Seat', were first published there. Thurber's humour is unique. Typically, his stories deal with the battle between the sexes – an apparently unequal fight between strong, dominating women and quiet, modest little men. Apart from his stories, Thurber is also well known for his cartoons and essays. A useful collection of his work is *The Thurber Carnival* (1945).

The story

Erwin Martin has been with F & S (the Fitweiler and Schlosser company) for over twenty years. During that time his work has been praised by everyone. Then one day Mrs Ulgine Barrows arrived . . .

The Catbird Seat

M R MARTIN bought the pack of Camels* on Monday night in the most crowded cigar store on Broadway*. It was theatre time and seven or eight men were buying cigarettes. The clerk didn't even glance at Mr Martin, who put the pack in his overcoat pocket and went out. If any of the staff at F & S had seen him buy the cigarettes, they would have been astonished, for it was generally known that Mr Martin did not smoke, and never had. No one saw him.

It was just a week to the day since Mr Martin had decided to rub out* Mrs Ulgine Barrows. The term 'rub out' pleased him because it suggested nothing more than the correction of an error – in this case an error of Mr Fitweiler. Mr Martin had spent each night of the past week working out his plan and examining it. As he walked home now he went over it again. For the hundredth time he resented the element of imprecision, the margin of guesswork that entered into the business. The project as he had worked it out was casual and bold, the risks were considerable. Something might go wrong anywhere along the line. And therein lay the cunning of his scheme. No one would ever see in it the cautious, painstaking hand of Erwin Martin, head of the filing department* at F & S, of whom Mr Fitweiler had once said, 'Man is fallible* but Martin isn't.' No one would see his hand, that is, unless it were caught in the act*.

Sitting in his apartment, drinking a glass of milk, Mr Martin reviewed his case* against Mrs Ulgine Barrows, as he had every night for seven nights. He began at the beginning. Her quacking voice and braying laugh* had first profaned* the halls of F & S on March 7, 1941 (Mr Martin had a head for dates). Old Roberts, the personnel chief, had introduced her as the newly appointed special adviser to the president of the firm, Mr Fitweiler. The woman had appalled* Mr Martin instantly, but he hadn't shown it. He had given her his dry hand, a look of studious* concentration, and a faint smile.

'Well,' she had said, looking at the papers on his desk, 'are you lifting the oxcart out of the ditch?' As Mr Martin recalled that moment, over his milk, he squirmed* slightly. He must keep his mind on her crimes as a special adviser, not on her peccadillos* as a personality. This he found difficult to do, in spite of entering an objection and sustaining it*. The faults of the woman as a woman kept chattering on in his mind like an unruly witness*. She had, for almost two years now, baited him*. In the halls, in the elevator, even in his own office, into which she romped* now and then like a circus horse, she was constantly shouting these silly questions at him. 'Are you lifting the oxcart out of the ditch? Are you tearing up the pea patch? Are you hollering down the rain barrel? Are you scraping around the bottom of the pickle barrel? Are you sitting in the catbird seat?'

It was Joey Hart, one of Mr Martin's two assistants, who had explained what the gibberish* meant. 'She must be a Dodger* fan,' he had said. 'Red Barber announces the Dodger games over the radio and he uses those expressions – picked 'em up down South*.' Joey had gone on to explain one or two. 'Tearing up the pea patch' meant going on a rampage*; 'sitting in the catbird seat' meant sitting pretty*, like a batter with three balls and no strikes on him*. Mr Martin dismissed all this with an effort. It had been annoying, it had driven him near to distraction, but he was too solid a man to be moved to murder by anything so childish. It was fortunate, he reflected as he passed on to the important charges against Mrs Barrows, that he had stood up under it so well. He had maintained always an outward appearance of polite tolerance. 'Why, I even believe you like the woman,' Miss Paird, his other assistant, had once said to him. He had simply smiled.

A gavel* rapped in Mr Martin's mind and the case proper was resumed. Mrs Ulgine Barrows stood charged with willful, blatant*, and persistent attempts to destroy the efficiency and system of F & S. It was competent, material, and relevant* to review her advent* and rise to power. Mr Martin had got the story from Miss Paird, who seemed always able to find things out. According to her, Mrs Barrows had met Mr Fitweiler at a party, where she had rescued him from the embraces of a powerfully built drunken man who had mistaken the president of F & S for a famous retired Middle Western* football coach. She had led him to a sofa and somehow worked upon him a monstrous magic. The aging gentlemen had jumped to the conclusion there and then that this was a woman of singular attainments*, equipped to bring out the best in him and in the firm. A week later he had introduced her into F & S as his special adviser. On that day confusion got its foot in the door. After Miss Tyson, Mr Brundage, and Mr Bartlett had been fired and Mr Munson had taken his hat and stalked out, mailing in his resignation later, old Roberts had been emboldened to speak to Mr Fitweiler. He mentioned that Mr Munson's department had been 'a little disrupted' and hadn't they perhaps better resume the old system there? Mr Fitweiler had said certainly not. He had the greatest faith in Mrs Barrows' ideas. 'They require a little seasoning*, a little seasoning, is all,' he had added. Mr Roberts had given it up. Mr Martin reviewed in detail all the changes wrought by Mrs Barrows. She had begun chipping at the cornices of the firm's edifice and now she was swinging at the foundation stones with a pickaxe*.

Mr Martin came now, in his summing up*, to the afternoon of Monday, November 2, 1942 – just one week ago. On that day, at 3 P.M., Mrs Barrows had bounced into his office. 'Boo!' she had yelled. 'Are you scraping around the bottom of the pickle barrel?' Mr Martin had looked at her from under his green eyeshade*, saying nothing. She had begun to wander about the office, taking it in with her great, popping eyes. 'Do you really need *all* these filing cabinets?' she had demanded suddenly. Mr Martin's heart had jumped. 'Each of these files,' he had said, keeping his voice even, 'plays an indispensable* part in the system of F & S.' She had brayed at him, 'Well, don't tear up the pea patch!' and gone to the door. From there she had bawled, 'But you sure have got a lot of fine scrap* in here!' Mr Martin could no longer doubt that the finger was on* his beloved department. Her pickaxe was on the upswing, poised for the first blow. It had not come yet; he had received no blue memo* from the enchanted Mr Fitweiler bearing nonsensical* instructions deriving from the obscene woman. But there was no doubt in Mr Martin's mind that one would be forthcoming. He must act quickly. Already a precious week had gone by. Mr Martin stood up in his living room, still holding his milk glass. 'Gentlemen of the jury*,' he said to himself, 'I demand the death penalty for this horrible person.'

The next day Mr Martin followed his routine, as usual. He polished his glasses more often and once sharpened an already sharp pencil, but not even Miss Paird noticed. Only once did he catch sight of his victim; she swept past him in the hall with a patronizing* 'Hi!' At five-thirty he walked home, as usual, and had a glass of milk, as usual. He had never drunk anything stronger in his life – unless you could count ginger ale. The late* Sam Schlosser, the S of F & S, had praised Mr Martin at a staff meeting several years before for his temperate habits. 'Our most efficient worker neither drinks nor smokes,' he had said. 'The results speak for themselves.' Mr Fitweiler had sat by, nodding approval.

Mr Martin was still thinking about the red-letter day* as he walked over to the Schrafft's on Fifth Avenue near Forty-Sixth Street. He got there, as he always did, at eight o'clock. He finished his dinner and the financial page of the *Sun* at a quarter to nine, as he always did. It was his custom after dinner to take a walk. This time he walked down Fifth Avenue at a casual pace. His gloved hands felt moist and warm, his forehead cold. He transferred the Camels from his overcoat to a jacket pocket. He wondered, as he did so, if they did not represent an unnecessary note of strain. Mrs Barrows smoked only Luckies*. It was his idea to puff a few puffs on a Camel (after the rubbing-out), stub it out in the ashtray holding her lipstick-stained Luckies, and thus drag a small red herring across the trail*. Perhaps it was not a good idea. It would take time. He might even choke* too loudly.

Mr Martin had never seen the house on West Twelfth Street where Mrs Barrows lived, but he had a clear enough picture of it. Fortunately, she had bragged* to everybody about her ducky* first-floor apartment in the perfectly darling three-storey red-brick*. There would be no doorman or other attendants; just the tenants of the second and third floors. As he walked along, Mr Martin realized that he would get there before nine-thirty. He had considered walking north on Fifth Avenue from Schrafft's to a point from which it would take him until ten o'clock to reach the house. At that hour people were less likely to be coming in or going out. But the procedure would have made an awkward loop in the straight thread of his casualness*, and he had abandoned it. It was impossible to figure when people would be entering or leaving the house, anyway. There was a great risk at any hour. If he ran into anybody, he would simply have to place the rubbing-out of Ulgine Barrows in the inactive file forever. The same thing would hold true if there were someone in her apartment. In that case he would just say that he had been passing by, recognized her charming house, and thought to drop in.

It was eighteen minutes after nine when Mr Martin turned into Twelfth Street. A man passed him, and a man and a woman, talking. There was no one within fifty paces when he came to the house, halfway down the block. He was up the steps and in the small vestibule* in no time, pressing the bell under the card that said 'Mrs Ulgine Barrows.' When the clicking in the lock started, he jumped forward against the door. He got inside fast, closing the door behind him. A bulb in a lantern hung from the hall ceiling on a chain seemed to give a monstrously bright light. There was nobody on the stair, which went up ahead of him along the left wall. A door opened down the hall in the wall on the right. He went toward it swiftly, on tiptoe.

'Well, for God's sake, look who's here!' bawled Mrs Barrows, and her braying laugh rang out like the report* of a shot-gun. He rushed past her like a football tackle*, bumping her. 'Hey, quit shoving!' she said, closing the door behind them. They were in her living room, which seemed to Mr Martin to be lighted by a hundred lamps. 'What's after you?' she said. 'You're as jumpy as a goat.' He found he was unable to speak. His heart was wheezing* in his throat. 'I – yes,' he finally brought out. She was jabbering* and laughing as she started to help him off with his coat. 'No, no,' he said. 'I'll put it here.' He took it off and put it on a chair near the door. 'Your hat and gloves, too,' she said. 'You're in a lady's house.' He put his hat on top of the coat. Mrs Barrows seemed larger than he had thought. He kept his gloves on. 'I was passing by,' he said. 'I recognized – is there anyone here?' She laughed louder than ever. 'No,' she said, 'we're all alone. You're as white as a sheet, you funny man. Whatever *has* come over you? I'll mix you a toddy*.' She started toward a door across the room. 'Scotch-and-soda be all right? But say, you don't drink, do you?' She turned and gave him her amused look. Mr Martin pulled himself together. 'Scotch-and-soda will be all right,' he heard himself say. He could hear her laughing in the kitchen.

Mr Martin looked quickly around the living room for the weapon. He had counted on finding one there. There were andirons* and a poker* and something in a corner that looked like an Indian club*. None of them would do. It couldn't be that way. He began to pace around. He came to a desk. On it lay a metal paper knife with an ornate handle. Would it be sharp enough? He reached for it and knocked over a small brass jar. Stamps spilled out of it and it fell to the floor with a clatter*. 'Hey,' Mrs Barrows yelled from the kitchen, 'are you tearing up the pea patch?' Mr Martin gave a strange laugh. Picking up the knife, he tried its point against his left wrist. It was blunt. It wouldn't do.

When Mrs Barrows reappeared, carrying two highballs*, Mr Martin, standing there with his gloves on, became acutely conscious of the fantasy he had wrought. Cigarettes in his pocket, a drink prepared for him – it was all too grossly improbable. It was more than that; it was impossible. Somewhere in the back of his mind a vague idea stirred, sprouted. 'For heaven's sake, take off those gloves,' said Mrs Barrows. 'I always wear them in the house,' said Mr Martin. The idea began to bloom, strange and wonderful. She put the glasses on a coffee table in front of a sofa and sat on the sofa. 'Come over here, you odd little man,' she said. Mr Martin went over and sat beside her. It was difficult getting a cigarette out of the pack of Camels, but he managed it. She held a match for him, laughing. 'Well,' she said, handing him his drink, 'this is perfectly marvelous. You with a drink and a cigarette.'

Mr Martin puffed, not too awkwardly, and took a gulp of the highball. 'I drink and smoke all the time,' he said. He clinked his glass against hers. 'Here's nuts to that old windbag, Fitweiler,' he said, and gulped again. The stuff tasted awful, but he made no grimace. 'Really, Mr Martin,' she said, her voice and posture changing, 'you are insulting our employer.' Mrs Barrows was now all special adviser to the president. 'I am preparing a bomb,' said Mr Martin, 'which will blow the old goat higher than hell.' He had only a little of the drink, which was not strong. It couldn't be that. 'Do you take dope* or something?' Mrs Barrows asked coldly. 'Heroin,' said Mr Martin. 'I'll be coked to the gills when I bump that old buzzard off*.' 'Mr Martin!' she shouted, getting to her feet. 'That will be all of that. You must go at once.' Mr Martin took another swallow of his drink. He tapped his cigarette out in the ashtray and put the pack of Camels on the coffee table. Then he got up. She stood glaring at him. He walked over and put on his hat and coat. 'Not a word about this,' he said, and laid an index finger against his lips. All Mrs Barrows could bring out was 'Really!' Mr Martin put his hand on the doorknob. 'I'm sitting in the catbird seat,' he said. He stuck his tongue out at her and left. Nobody saw him go.

Mr Martin got to his apartment, walking, well before eleven. No one saw him go in. He had two glasses of milk after brushing his teeth, and he felt elated*. It wasn't tipsiness*, because he hadn't been tipsy. Anyway, the walk had worn off all effects of the whisky. He got in bed and read a magazine for a while. He was asleep before midnight.

Mr Martin got to the office at eight-thirty the next morning, as usual. At a quarter to nine, Ulgine Barrows, who had never before arrived at work before ten, swept into his office 'I'm reporting to Mr Fitweiler now!' she shouted. 'If he turns you over to the police, it's no more than you deserve!' Mr Martin gave her a look of shocked surprise. 'I beg your pardon?' he said. Mrs Barrows snorted and bounced out of the room, leaving Miss Paird and Joey Hart staring after her. 'What's the matter with that old devil now?' asked Miss Paird. 'I have no idea,' said Mr Martin, resuming his work. The other two looked at him and then at each other. Miss Paird got up and went out. She walked slowly past the closed door of Mr Fitweiler's office. Mrs Barrows was yelling inside, but she was not braying. Miss Paird could not hear what the woman was saying. She went back to her desk.

Forty-five minutes later, Mrs Barrows left the president's office and went into her own, shutting the door. It wasn't until half an hour later that Mr Fitweiler sent for Mr Martin. The head of the filing department, neat, quiet, attentive, stood in front of the old man's desk. Mr Fitweiler was pale and nervous. He took his glasses off and twiddled* them. He made a small, bruffing* sound in his throat. 'Martin,' he said, 'you have been with us more than twenty years.' 'Twenty-two, sir,' said Mr Martin. 'In that time,' pursued the president, 'your work and your – uh – manner have been exemplary*.' 'I trust so, sir,' said Mr Martin. 'I have understood, Martin,' said Mr Fitweiler, 'that you have never taken a drink or smoked.' 'That is correct, sir,' said Mr Martin. 'Ah, yes.' Mr Fitweiler polished his glasses. 'You may describe what you did after leaving the office yesterday, Martin,' he said. Mr Martin allowed less than a second for his bewildered pause. 'Certainly, sir,' he said. 'I walked home. Then I went to Schrafft's for dinner. Afterward I walked home again. I went to bed early, sir, and read a magazine for a while. I was asleep before eleven.' 'Ah, yes,' said Mr Fitweiler again. He was silent for a moment, searching for the proper words to say to the head of the filing department. 'Mrs Barrows,' he said finally, 'Mrs Barrows has worked hard, Martin, very hard. It grieves me to report that she has suffered a severe breakdown. It has taken the form of a persecution complex* accompanied by distressing hallucinations*.' 'I am very sorry, sir,' said Mr Martin. 'Mrs Barrows is under the delusion,' continued Mr Fitweiler, 'that you visited her last evening and behaved yourself in an – uh – unseemly* manner.' He raised his hand to silence

Mr Martin's little pained outcry. 'It is the nature of these psychological diseases,' Mr Fitweiler said, 'to fix upon the least likely and most innocent party as the – uh – source of persecution. These matters are not for the lay* mind to grasp, Martin. I've just had my psychiatrist, Doctor Fitch, on the phone. He would not, of course, commit himself, but he made enough generalizations to substantiate my suspicions. I suggested to Mrs Barrows, when she had completed her – uh – story to me this morning, that she visit Doctor Fitch, for I suspected a condition at once. She flew, I regret to say, into a rage, and demanded – uh – requested that I call you on the carpet*. You may not know, Martin, but Mrs Barrows had planned a reorganization of your department – subject to my approval, of course, subject to my approval. This brought you, rather than anyone else, to her mind – but again that is a phenomenon for Doctor Fitch and not for us. So, Martin, I am afraid Mrs Barrows' usefulness here is at an end.' 'I am dreadfully sorry, sir,' said Mr Martin.

It was at this point that the door to the office blew open with the suddenness of a gas-main explosion and Mrs Barrows catapulted* through it. 'Is the little rat denying it?' she screamed. 'He can't get away with that!' Mr Martin got up and moved discreetly to a point beside Mr Fitweiler's chair. 'You drank and smoked at my apartment,' she bawled at Mr Martin, 'and you know it! You called Mr Fitweiler an old windbag and said you were going to blow him up when you got coked to the gills on your heroin!' She stopped yelling to catch her breath and a new glint came into her popping eyes. 'If you weren't such a drab*, ordinary little man,' she said. 'I'd think you'd planned it all. Sticking your tongue out, saying you were sitting in the catbird seat, because you thought no one would believe me when I told it! My God, it's really too perfect!' She brayed loudly and hysterically, and the fury was on her again. She glared at Mr Fitweiler. 'Can't you see how he has tricked us, you old fool? Can't you see his little game?' But Mr Fitweiler had been surreptitiously* pressing all the buttons under the top of his desk and employees of F & S began pouring into the room. 'Stockton,' said Mr Fitweiler, 'you and Fishbein will take Mrs Barrows to her home. Mrs Powell, you will go with them.' Stockton, who had played a little football in high school, blocked* Mrs Barrows as she made for Mr Martin. It took him and Fishbein together to force her out of the door into the hall, crowded with stenographers* and office boys. She was still screaming imprecations* at Mr Martin, tangled and contradictory imprecations. The hubbub* finally died down the corridor.

'I regret that this has happened,' said Mr Fitweiler. 'I shall ask you to dismiss it from your mind, Martin.' 'Yes, sir,' said Mr Martin, anticipating his chief's 'That will be all' by moving to the door. 'I will dismiss it.' He went out and shut the door, and his step was light and quick in the hall. When he entered his department he had slowed down to his customary gait*, and he walked quietly across the room to the W20 file, wearing a look of studious concentration.

Glossary

The meanings given below are those which the words and phrases have as they occur in the story.

Page

109   *Camels*: an American brand of cigarette.

Broadway: the entertainment area of New York.

rub out (Am.E.sl.): murder.

filing department: department of a business organization where company papers are organized and stored.

fallible: capable of making mistakes.

caught in the act: found when actually doing something wrong.

reviewed his case: thought over the facts of the case (as a lawyer would before arguing the case in court).

quacking voice and braying laugh: both 'quacking' and 'braying' are loud unpleasant noises, the former associated with ducks, the latter with donkeys.

profaned: dishonoured, treated disrespectfully.

appalled: deeply shocked.

studious: careful.

110   *squirmed*: twisted his body about with embarrassment.

peccadillos: unimportant faults.

entering an objection and sustaining it (legal language): objecting to his thoughts about Mrs Barrows' personality, and recognizing that the objection was correct.

unruly witness: a witness in a court of law who cannot be controlled.

baited him: deliberately made him angry.

romped: walked in with much noise and activity.

gibberish: meaningless words.

Dodger: The Dodgers – a famous New York baseball team.

South: Southern states of the United States. The people there are well known for their colourful colloquial expressions, often using words and ideas associated with life on farms and in the country.

going on a rampage: acting excitedly and violently.

sitting pretty: being in a fortunate situation.

batter . . . no strikes on him: a good situation to be in if you are batting in a baseball match.

gavel: small hammer used by a judge to get attention.

blatant: very obvious, shameless.

competent, material, and relevant: i.e. it was the right time and place to consider her arrival on the scene and her rise to power. Mr Martin puts his thoughts in language appropriate to a court of law.

advent: arrival.

111   *Middle Western*: the north central part of the United States.

singular attainments: outstanding special skills.

seasoning: time for the ideas to work.

chipping at the cornices . . . with a pickaxe: the image here is of someone knocking down a building, at first using small blows, and then large damaging blows. A pickaxe is a large tool with sharp pointed ends made of iron that is used to break up roads, rocks etc.

summing up: the final comments by a lawyer at the end of a court case.

eyeshade: a cover worn over the eyes (by clerks, for example) to keep out bright light (not often used today).

indispensable: absolutely necessary.

scrap: rubbish, unimportant and unnecessary pieces of paper.

the finger was on: his department was threatened.

memo: a note sent from one person to another within a business organization.

nonsensical: meaningless.

112   *jury*: group of (usually 12) people who decide if a person is guilty or not guilty in a court of law.

patronizing: speaking as if to an inferior person.

late: someone who has recently died.

red-letter day: a specially important day that will be remembered.

Luckies: Lucky Strikes, a fashionable brand of cigarette.

drag a small red herring across the trail: introduce a false clue.

choke: the cigarette might make him cough badly and make it difficult for him to breathe.

bragged: boasted.

ducky: delightful (a word generally used by women rather than men).

red-brick (Am.E): the apartment block which she lives in is built of red bricks. In New York these buildings are considered fashionable and are generally owned by the more wealthy.

113 *awkward loop in the straight thread of his casualness*: his plan would not be as casual and uncomplicated as he wanted it to be.

vestibule: entrance hall.

report: noise of the gun going off.

football tackle (Am.E): a tackle is a forward player in American football. Mr Martin rushes in as though making an aggressive forward charge in a game of American football.

wheezing: making a noisy sound.

jabbering: talking excitedly and unclearly.

114 *toddy*: an alcoholic drink.

andirons: metal supports in a fireplace on which logs are burnt.

poker: a metal bar used to break up or move coal or wood in a fireplace.

Indian club: a wooden club used in gymnastic exercises.

clatter: loud noise.

highballs (Am.E.): whisky and sodas.

115 *dope*: drugs.

I'll be coked . . . that old buzzard off (sl.): I'll be full of drugs when I murder the old man. A buzzard in American English is a type of vulture (a bird which feeds on dead animals).

elated: full of pride and joy.

tipsiness: slight drunkenness.

116 *twiddled*: purposelessly played with his glasses with his fingers.

bruffing: a word invented by Thurber. It suggests a short embarrassed cough.

exemplary: a model, an example for others.

persecution complex: a false belief that other people want to be unpleasant to you.

hallucinations: imagined thoughts caused by mental illness.

unseemly: improper, unsuitable.

117   *lay*: unspecialized. Here it means someone who is not trained in psychiatry.

call you on the carpet (idiom.): speak to you severely and officially about something you have done wrong.

catapulted: rushed wildly in.

drab: uninteresting, boring.

surreptitiously: secretly.

118   *blocked (Am.E)*: a term used in American football meaning to forcefully stop another player from moving forward.

stenographers (Am.E): typists.

imprecations: curses, swearing.

hubbub: loud, confused noises.

gait: way of walking.

Questions

1. In what ways are Mr Martin and Mrs Barrows very different people?

   (a) What are the usual drinking and smoking habits of Mrs Barrows and Mr Martin? (pp. 112, 114)

   (b) What are Mrs Barrows' voice, laughter and movements like? (pp. 109–10) Martin has a 'dry hand, a look of studious concentration and a faint smile' when he meets Mrs Barrows. (p. 109) What does that tell us about him?

   (c) What interests does Mrs Barrows have outside work? (p. 110) What does Mr Martin do in the evenings? (p. 112) What do these activities reveal about their characters?

2. Why does Mr Martin change his murder plans?

   (a) Why does Martin think that the false clue with the cigarette may not be a good idea? (p. 112)

   (b) Why is mention made of the hall light which 'seemed to give a monstrously bright light', the living room which 'seemed . . . be lighted by a hundred lamps' and Mrs Barrows who 'seemed larger than he had thought'? (pp. 113–4)

   (c) Make a list of the things that Mr Fitweiler would find impossible to believe about Martin's behaviour at Mrs Barrows' apartment.

Language Activities

Point of View

In 'The Catbird Seat' the reader sees and experiences things very much from Mr Martin's point of view.

Take the second paragraph of the story and write down Mr Martin's thoughts as they come to him. You could begin, for example, 'Yes, it was a week ago I decided "to rub her out". "To rub her out": what a lovely expression that is! . . .'

Images

(a) What area of language (e.g. the law, business etc.) are the following words usually associated with?

   (i)   quacking, braying.

   (ii) the inactive file.

   (iii) entering an objection and sustaining it.

   (iv) cornice, edifice, foundation stone.

(b) A number of images are used in 'The Catbird Seat', the most developed being Mr Martin's thoughts about Mrs Barrows' 'crimes'. The image is of Martin as a lawyer and Mrs Barrows as the accused in a court of law.

   Explain the following in simple, everyday language.

Note the context in which they appear:

(i)   'A gavel rapped in Mr Martin's mind and the case proper was resumed.' (p. 110)

(ii) 'Her pickaxe was on the upswing, poised for the first blow.' (p. 111)

(iii) 'If he ran into anybody, he would simply have to place the rubbing-out in the inactive file forever.' (p. 113)

Ideas for Writing

1. Write the report Mr Fitweiler's psychiatrist, Dr. Fitch, might send to Mr Fitweiler after having examined Mrs Barrows. Begin 'Dear Mr Fitweiler, I examined Mrs Ulgine Barrows today and . . .'

2. Mr Martin decides to take early retirement. Write out the speech that Mr Fitweiler would make at the retirement party. Begin 'It is sad for us all that this is the last time Erwin Martin will enter this building as an employee of F & S . . .'

* * * * * *

1. Which of these two stories do you prefer? What are some of the reasons for your choice?

2. 'When we have found out what happens in these stories, they are not worth reading again.' Discuss this statement, making clear whether you agree with it or not.

Loneliness

Susan Hill

Susan Hill, born in 1942, is a contemporary English writer whose novels and short stories have in recent years gained a wide readership. She won the Somerset Maugham Award in 1971 for *I'm the King of the Castle*, the John Llewellyn Rhys Prize for *The Albatross and Other Stories*, and the Whitbread Award (1972) for *The Bird Of Night*. Susan Hill's stories are often about children and old people, whose experiences, frequently of a dark kind, she explores with great insight and sensitivity. 'How Soon Can I Leave?' is taken from a collection of stories entitled *A Bit of Singing and Dancing* (1975).

The story

Miss Roscommon and Miss Bartlett are two middle-aged ladies who live together in the small English seaside town of Mountsea. They seem to be a suitable couple – Miss Bartlett is the artistic one and Miss Roscommon is the practical one – but as the years go by Miss Bartlett begins to want to break free . . .

How Soon Can I Leave?

T HE two ladies who lived together were called Miss
Bartlett and Miss Roscommon.

Miss Roscommon, the older and stouter* of the two, con-
cealed her fear of life behind frank* reference to babies and
lavatories and the sexing* of day-old chicks. It was well known
that she had travelled widely as a girl, she told of her walking
tours in Greece, and how she had driven an ambulance during
the Spanish Civil War*.

Miss Bartlett, who was only forty, cultivated* shyness and
self-effacement, out of which arose her way of leaving muttered sentences to trail off into the air, unfinished. Oh, do not
take any notice of anything *I* may say, she meant, it is of no
consequence, I am sorry to have spoken . . . But the sentences
drew attention to her, nevertheless.

'What was that?' people said, 'I beg your pardon, I didn't
quite catch . . . Do speak up . . .' And so, she was forced to
repeat herself and they, having brought it upon themselves,
were forced to listen. She also protested helplessness in the
face of everyday tools. It was Miss Roscommon who peeled all
the potatoes and defrosted the refrigerator and opened the
tins.

Their house, one of two white bungalows* overlooking the
bay, was called Tuscany.

When Miss Bartlett had finally come to live with Miss
Roscommon, seven years before, each one believed that the
step was taken for the good of the other. Miss Bartlett had
been living in one of the little stone cottages, opposite the
harbour*, working through the winter on the stock that she
sold, from her front room and on a trestle* outside, in summer. From November until March, there were no visitors to
Mountsea. Winds and rain scoured* the surface of the cliffs
and only the lifeboat* put out to sea. Miss Roscommon had
taken to inviting Miss Bartlett up to the bungalow for meals.

'You should have a shop,' she had begun by saying, loading

Miss Bartlett's plate with scones* and home-made ginger jam, 'properly equipped and converted. It cannot be satisfactory having to display goods in your living-room. Why have you not thought of taking a shop?'

Miss Bartlett made marquetry* pictures of the church, the lighthouse and the harbour, table-lamps out of lobster pots* and rocks worked over with shells. She also imported Italian straw baskets and did a little pewter* work.

The idea of a shop had come to her, and been at once dismissed, in the first weeks after her coming to Mountsea. She was too timid to take any so definite a step, for, by establishing herself in a shop, with her name written up on a board outside, was she not establishing herself in the minds of others, as a shop*keeper*? As a girl, she had been impressed by her mother's constant references to her as dreamy and artistic, so that she could not possibly now see herself in the role of shopkeeper. Also, by having her name written up on that board, she felt that she would somehow be committing herself to Mountsea, and by doing that, finally abandoning all her hopes of a future in some other place. As a girl, she had looked out at the world, and seen a signpost, with arms pointing in numerous different directions, roads leading here, or here, or there. She had been quite unable to choose which road to take for, having once set out upon any of them, she would thereby be denying herself all the others. And what might I lose, she had thought, what opportunities shall I miss if I make the wrong choice?

So that, in the end, she had never chosen, only drifted* through her life from this to that, waking every morning to the expectation of some momentous good fortune dropped in her lap*.

'That cottage is damp,' said Miss Roscommon, allowing her persuasions to take on a more personal note, as they got to know one another better. 'I do not think you look after yourself properly. And a place of business should not have to double as a home.'

At first, Miss Bartlett shrank from the hints and persuasions, knowing herself to be easily swayed*, fearful of being swept along on the tide* of Miss Roscommon's decision. I am forty years old, she said, there is plenty of opportunity left for me, I do not have to abandon hope by retreating into middle age, and life with another woman. Though certainly she enjoyed the meals the other cooked; the taste of home-baked pasties* and stews and herb-flavoured vegetables.

'I'm afraid that I cannot cook,' she said. 'I live on milk and cheese and oven-baked potatoes. I would not know where to begin in the kitchen.' It did not occur to her that this was any cause for shame, and Miss Roscommon tut-tutted* and floured the pastry-board, relieved to have, once again, a sense of purpose brought into her life.

'There were nine of us in the family,' she said, 'and I was the only girl. At the age of seven, I knew how to bake a perfect loaf of bread. I am quite content to be one of the Marthas* of this world.'

But I will not go and *live* there, Miss Bartlett told herself, towards the end of that summer. I am determined to remain independent, my plans are fluid*, I have my work, and besides, it would never do, we might not get on well together and then it would be embarrassing for me to have to leave. And people might talk.

Though she knew that they would not, and that it was of her own judgement that she was most afraid, for Mountsea was full of ladies of indeterminate* age, sharing houses together.

The winter came, and the cottage was indeed damp. The stone walls struck cold all day and all night, in spite of expensive electric heaters, and Miss Bartlett spent longer and longer afternoons at Tuscany, even taking some of her work up there, from time to time.

At the beginning of December, the first of the bad storms sent waves crashing up over the quayside* into the front room.

Of course, Miss Roscommon is lonely, she said now, she has need of me, I should have realized. That type of woman, who appears to be so competent and strong, feels the onset of old age and infirmity* more than most, but she cannot say so, cannot give way and confess to human weakness. She bakes me cakes and worries about the dampness in my house because she needs my company and concern for herself.

And so, on Christmas Eve, when the second storm filled Miss Bartlett's living room with water up to the level of the window seat, she allowed herself to be evacuated* by the capable Miss Roscommon up to the white bungalow.

'It will not be for good,' she said anxiously, 'when the weather improves, I shall have to go back, there is the business to be thought of.' 'We shall make plans for a proper shop,' said Miss Roscommon firmly, 'I have a little money . . .'

She filled up a pottery bowl with leek* soup, having acquired her faith in its restorative* powers when she had set up a canteen* at the scene of a mining disaster in the nineteen-twenties.

Miss Bartlett accepted the soup and a chair close to the fire and an electric blanket for her bed, thereby setting the seal on* the future pattern of their relationship. By the beginning of February, plans for the shop were made, by mid-March, the work was in hand. There was no longer any talk of her moving, she would sell her goods from the new shop during the summer days, but she would live at Tuscany. The garage was fitted with light, heat and two extra windows, and made into a studio*.

'This is quite the best arrangement,' said Miss Roscommon, 'here, you will be properly fed and looked after, I shall see to that.'

Over the seven years that followed, Miss Bartlett came to rely upon her for many more things than the comforts of a well-kept home. It was Miss Roscommon who made all the business arrangements for the new shop, who saw the bank manager, the estate agent* and the builder, Miss Roscommon who advised with the orders and the accounts. During the summer seasons, the shop did well, and after three years, at her friend's suggestion, Miss Bartlett started to make pink raffia* angels and potpourri* jars, for the Christmas postal market.

She relaxed, ceased to feel uneasy, and if, from time to time, she did experience a sudden shot of alarm, at seeing herself so well and truly settled, she said, not, 'Where else would I go?' but, 'I am needed here. However would she manage without me? It would be cruel to go.' All the decisions were left to Miss

Roscommon. 'You are so much better at these things . . .' Miss Bartlett said, and drifted away to her studio, a small woman with pastel-coloured* flesh.

Perhaps it was her forty-seventh birthday that jolted* her into a renewed awareness of the situation. She looked into the mirror on that morning, and saw middle-age settled irrevocably* over her features. She was reminded of her dependence upon Miss Roscommon.

I said I would not stay here, she thought, would never have my name written up above a permanent shop, for my plans were to remain fluid. And now it is seven years, and how many opportunities have I missed? How many roads are closed to me?

Or perhaps it was the visit of Miss Roscommon's niece Angela, and her husband of only seven days, one weekend in early September.

'I shall do a great deal of baking,' Miss Roscommon said, 'for they will certainly stay to tea. We shall have cheese scones and preserves* and a layer cake.'

'I did not realize that you had a niece.'

Miss Roscommon rose from the table heavily, for she had put on weight, over the seven years. There had also been some suspicion about a cataract* in her left eye, another reason why Miss Bartlett told herself she could not leave her.

'She is my youngest brother's child. I haven't seen her since she was a baby.'

Miss Bartlett nodded and wandered away from the breakfast table, not liking to ask why there had been no wedding invitation. Even after seven years, Miss Roscommon kept some of her secrets, there were subjects upon which she simply did not speak, though Miss Bartlett had long ago bared her own soul*.

The niece Angela, and her new husband, brought a slab of wedding cake, which was put to grace* the centre of the table on a porcelain stand.

'And this,' said Miss Roscommon triumphantly, '*this* is my friend, Miss Mary Bartlett.' For Miss Bartlett had hung behind in the studio for ten minutes after their arrival, out of courtesy* and because it was always something of a strain* for her to meet new people.

'Mary is very shy, very retiring,' her own mother had always said, 'she is artistic you see, she lives in her own world.' Her tone had always been proud and Miss Bartlett had therefore come to see her own failure as a mark of distinction. Her shyness had been cultivated, readily admitted to.

The niece and her husband sat together on the sofa, a little flushed* and self-conscious in new clothes. Seeing them there, Miss Bartlett realized for the first time that no young people had ever been inside the bungalow, since her arrival. But it was more than their youthfulness which struck her, there was an air of suppressed* excitement about them, a glitter*, they emanated* pride in the satisfactions of the flesh.

Miss Roscommon presided over* a laden tea-table, her face still flushed from the oven.

'And Miss Bartlett is very clever,' she told them, 'she makes beautiful things. You must go down to the shop and see them, buy something for your new home.'

'You make things?' said Angela, through a mouthful of shortbread*, 'what sort of things?'

Miss Bartlett made a little gesture of dismissal* with her hand. 'Oh, not very much really, nothing at all exciting. Just a few little . . . I'm sure you wouldn't . . .' She let her voice trail off, but it was Miss Roscommon and not the niece Angela who took her up on it.

'Now that is just nonsense,' she said firmly. 'There is no virtue in this false modesty, I have told you before. Of course Angela will like your things, why should she not? Plenty of visitors do, and there is nothing to be ashamed of in having a talent.'

'I wore a hand-embroidered dress,' said the niece Angela, 'for my wedding.'

Miss Bartlett watched her, and watched the new husband, whose eyes followed Angela's slim hand as it moved over to the cake plate and back, and up into her mouth. Their eyes met and shone with secrets, across the table. Miss Bartlett's stomach moved a little, with fear and excitement. She felt herself to be within touching distance of some very important piece of knowledge.

'Do you help with this shop, then – ?' asked the husband though without interest.

'Oh, no! Well, here and there with the accounts and so forth, because Mary doesn't understand any of that, she is such a dreamer! No, no, that is not my job, that is not what keeps me so busy. My job is to look after Mary, of course. I took that upon myself quite some time ago, when I saw that I was needed. She is such a silly girl, she lives in a world of her own and if I were not here to worry about her meals and her comforts, she would starve*, I assure you, simply starve.'

'Oh, I don't think I really . . .'

'Of course you would,' said Miss Roscommon. 'Now let me have your cup to be filled.'

The young couple exchanged another glance, of comprehension and amusement. How dare you, thought Miss Bartlett, almost in tears with anger and frustration*, at being so looked upon and judged and misunderstood. What do you know of it, how can you sit there so smugly*? It is because you are young and know nothing. It is all very well for you.

'All the same,' said the niece Angela, sitting back in her chair, 'it's nice to be looked after, I must say.'

She smiled like a cat.

'Yes, that has always been my role in life, that is *my* talent,' said Miss Roscommon, 'to do all the looking after.' She leaned over and patted Miss Bartlett on the hand. 'She is my responsibility now, you see,' she told them confidently. 'My little pussy-cat.'

Miss Bartlett pushed the hand away and got to her feet, her face flushed with shame and annoyance. 'What a foolish thing to say! Of course I am not, how very silly you make me look. I am a grown woman, I am quite capable of looking after myself.'

Miss Roscommon, not in the least discomfited*, only began to pour the tea dregs into a slop basin*, smiling.

When they were about to leave, Miss Bartlett said, 'I will walk down the hill with you, and we shall drop in for a minute at the shop. Yes, I insist . . . But not for you to buy anything. You must choose a wedding present from my stock, it is the very least I can do.' For she wanted to keep them with her longer, to be seen walking in their company down the hill away from the bungalow, wanted to be on their side.

'You will need a warm coat, it is autumn now, the evenings are drawing in*. Take your mohair*.'

'Oh, leave me, leave me, do not *fuss**.' And Miss Bartlett walked to the end of the gravelled drive, while the niece and her new husband made their good-byes.

'I am afraid it is all she has to worry over nowadays,' she said hastily, the moment they had joined her. 'It gives her pleasure, I suppose to do all that clucking round* and I have not the heart to do anything but play along, keep up appearances. If it were not for me, she would be so lonely. Of course, I have had to give up a good deal of my own life, on that account.'

The niece Angela took her husband's arm. 'It must be very nice and comfortable for you there,' she said, 'all the same.'

Miss Bartlett turned her face away and looked out to sea. Another winter, she thought, and I am now forty-seven years old. You do not understand.

She detained* them in the shop for as long as possible, fetching out special items from the stock room and taking time over the wrapping paper. Let me be with you, she wanted to say, let me be on your side, for do you not see that I still have many opportunities left, I am not an old woman, I know about the world and the ways of modern life? Take me with you.

But when they had gone she stood in the darkening shop and saw that they had already placed and dismissed her, that she did not belong with them and there was no hope left. She sat on the stool beside the till* and wept, for the injustice of the world and the weakness of her own nature. I have become what I always dreaded* becoming, she said, everything has slipped through my fingers.

And for all of it, after a short time, she began to blame Miss Roscommon. She has stifled* me, she thought, she preys upon* me, I am treated as her child, her toy, her *pussy-cat*, she has humiliated* me and fed off my dependence and the fact that I have always been so sensitive. She is a wicked woman. And then she said, *but I do not have to stay with her*. Fortified* by the truth of this new realization, Miss Bartlett blew her nose, and walked back up the hill to Tuscany.

'You cannot leave,' said Miss Roscommon, 'what nonsense, of course you cannot. You have nowhere else to go and besides in ten days' time we set off for our holiday in Florence.'

'You will set off. I am afraid my plans have now changed.' Miss Bartlett could not now bear the thought of being seen with her friend in all the museums and art galleries of Florence, discussing the paintings in loud, knowledgeable voices and eating wholemeal* sandwiches out of neat little greaseproof bags, speaking very slowly to the Italians. This year Miss Roscommon must go alone. She did not allow herself to think of how, or whether she would enjoy herself. We are always hearing of how intrepid* she was as a girl, she thought. Then let her be intrepid again.

Aloud, she said, 'I am going back to live at the cottage.' For she had kept it on, and rented it to summer visitors.

Miss Roscommon turned herself, and her darning*, a little more towards the light. 'You are being very foolish,' she said mildly. 'But I understand why, it is your age, of course.'

Appalled*, Miss Bartlett went through to her room, and began to throw things furiously, haphazardly*, into a suitcase. I am my own mistress, she said, a grown-up woman with years ahead of me, it is time for me to be firm. I have pandered to* her long enough.

The following day, watched by Miss Roscommon, she moved back down the hill to the cottage. She would, she decided, stay there for a while, give herself time to get accustomed, and to gather all of her things around her again, and then she would look out and make plans, take steps towards her new life.

That evening, hearing the wind around her own four walls, she said, I have escaped. Though she woke in the night and was aware of being entirely alone in the cottage, of not being able to hear the loud breathing of Miss Roscommon in the room next door.

She expected the Italian holiday to be cancelled, on some pretext*, and was astonished when Miss Roscommon left, on the appointed day and alone. Miss Bartlett took the opportunity of going up to Tuscany and fetching some more of her things down, work from the studio to keep her busy in the evening, and during the days, too, for now it was October and few people came into the shop.

Here I am, she said, twisting the raffia angels and winding ribbon around the pot-pourris, etching* her gift cards, here I am, living my own life and making my own decisions. She wanted to invite someone down to stay, someone young, so that she could be seen and approved of, but there was no one. A search through all the drawers and cupboards at the bungalow did not yield* her the address of the niece Angela. She would have sent a little note, with a Christmas gift, to tell of her removal, prove her independence.

Miss Roscommon returned from Italy, looked rather tired and not very suntanned. She came in with a miniature plaster copy of a Donatello* statue, and some fine art post-cards. Miss Bartlett made tea, and the conversation was very stilted*.

'You are not warm enough here,' said Miss Roscommon, 'I will send down some extra blankets.'

'Oh no, thank you. Please don't do that.'

But the following day the blankets, and a Dutch apple pie, arrived with the butcher's boy.

Miss Bartlett bought huge slabs of cheese and eggs, which she could boil quite well, and many potatoes, and ate them off her knee while she read detective stories through the long evenings. She thought that she might buy a television set for company, though she was busy too, with the postal orders for Christmas. When all this is over, she told herself, that is when I shall start looking about me and making my plans. She thought of all the things she might have done as a girl, the studio in London and the woodblock engravings* for the poetry press*, the ballet company for whom she might have been asked to do some ethereal* costume designs. She read in a newspaper of a woman who had started her own firm, specializing in computer management, at the age of fifty and was now rather wealthy, wholly respected in a man's world. Miss Bartlett looked at herself in the mirror. I am only forty-seven, she said.

In her white bungalow, lonely and lacking a sense of purpose, Miss Roscommon waited.

On November the seventh, the first of the storms came, and Miss Bartlett sat in her back room and heard the wind and the crashing of the sea, terrified. The next morning, she saw that part of the pierhead* had broken away. Miss Roscommon sent down a note, with a meat pasty, via the butcher's boy.

'I am worried about you,' she wrote, 'you cannot be looking after yourself, and I know that it is damp in that cottage. Your room here is ready for you at any time.'

Miss Bartlett tore the note up and threw the pasty away, but she thought of the warm bed, the fires and soft sofas at Tuscany.

Two days later, when the gales* began again, Miss Roscommon came herself, and hammered at the door of the cottage, but Miss Bartlett hid upstairs, behind a cheval mirror*, until she went away. This time, there was no note, only a thermos flask* of lentil* soup on the doorstep.

She is suffocating me*, thought Miss Bartlett, I cannot bear all these unwanted attentions, I only wish to be left alone. It is a poor thing if a woman of her age and resources can find nothing else to occupy her, nothing else to live for. But in spite of herself, she drank the soup, and the taste of it, the smell of the steam rising up into her face reminded her of all the meals at Tuscany, the winter evenings spent happily sitting beside the fire.

When the storms came again, another section of the pier broke away, the lifeboat put out to sea and sank with all hands*, and the front room of Miss Bartlett's cottage was flooded, rain broke in through a rent* in the roof. She lay all night, too terrified by the roaring of the wind and seas to get out of bed and do anything about it, only whimpering* a little with cold and fright, remembering how close the cottage came to the water, how vulnerable* she was.

As a child, she had been afraid of all storms, gales and thunder and cloudbursts drumming on the roof, and her mother had understood, wrapped her in a blanket and taken her into her own bed.

'It is because you have such a vivid imagination,' she had said, 'you feel things that the other, ordinary little children, cannot ever feel.' And so, nothing had been done to conquer this praiseworthy fear of storms.

Now, I am alone, thought Miss Bartlett, there is no one, my mother is dead, and who is there to shelter and understand me? A flare rocket*, sent up from the sinking lifeboat, lit up the room faintly for a second, and then she knew who there was, and that everything would be all right. On the stormy nights, Miss Roscommon always got up and made sandwiches and milky hot drinks, brought them to her as she lay awake in bed, and they would sit reading nice magazines, in the gentle circle of the bedside lamp.

I have been very foolish, Miss Bartlett thought, and heard herself saying it aloud, humbly, to Miss Roscommon. A very foolish, selfish woman, I do not deserve to have you as a friend.

She did not take very much with her up the hill on the following morning, only a little handcase and some raffia work. The rest could follow later, and it would be better to arrive like that, it would be a real indication of her helplessness.

The landscape was washed very clean and bare and pale, but the sea churned* and moved within itself, angry and battleship grey. In the summer, Miss Bartlett thought, refreshed again by the short walk, it will be time to think again, for I am not committing myself to any permanent arrangements and things will have to be rather different now, I will not allow myself to be treated as a pet plaything, that must be understood. For she had forgotten, in the cold, clear morning, the terrors of the previous night.

She wondered what to do, ring the bell or knock or simply open the door into the kitchen, where Miss Roscommon would be working, and stand there, case in hand, waiting to be forgiven. Her heart beat a little faster. Tuscany was very settled and reassuring* in its low, four-square whiteness on top of the hill. Miss Bartlett knocked timidly at the blue kitchen door.

It was some time before she gave up knocking and ringing, and simply went in. Tuscany was very quiet.

She found her in the living-room, lying crumpled* awkwardly on the floor, one of her legs twisted underneath her. Her face was a curious, flat colour, like the inside of a raw potato. Miss Bartlett drew back the curtains. The clock had stopped just before midnight, almost twelve hours ago.

For a moment, she stood there, still holding her little case, in the comfortable, chintzy* room and then she dropped down on to her knees, and took the head of Miss Roscommon into her lap and, rocking and rocking, cradling* it like a child, Miss Bartlett wept.

Glossary

The meanings given below are those which the words and phrases have as they occur in the story.

Page

127   *stouter*: fatter.

frank: open, direct.

sexing: telling whether the chickens are male or female.

Spanish Civil War: war in Spain, 1936–9.

cultivated: encouraged in herself.

bungalows: one-storey (i.e. one-floor) houses.

harbour: place of shelter for boats.

trestle: a type of table.

scoured: wore away.

lifeboat: boat used for saving people in danger at sea.

128   *scones*: a type of small cake.

marquetry: pictures made with pieces of coloured wood.

lobster pots: traps shaped like baskets in which lobsters (a sea animal) are caught.

pewter: a type of metal

drifted: moved along without purpose.

dropped in her lap: came to her by chance, without her working for it.

swayed: influenced.

swept along on the tide: unable to fight against, totally influenced by.

129   *pasties*: a type of small (usually meat) pie.

tut-tutted: a noise made by the tongue to show one does not approve.

Marthas: a helper of others. Martha serves Jesus in the Bible.

fluid: not fixed.

indeterminate: difficult to judge.

quayside: place built of stone where boats can land and tie up.

infirmity: weakness, illness.

130   *evacuated*: moved out of the house out of danger.

leek: a vegetable similar to an onion.

restorative: bringing back strength.

canteen: temporary place where food is given out.

setting the seal on: deciding, making official.

studio: well-lit room where art work can be done.

estate agent: person who deals with the business of buying and selling houses and land for others.

raffia: a grass-like material used for making things e.g. small figures.

pot-pourri: dried pieces of sweet-smelling flowers.

131 *pastel-coloured*: a soft, light colour.

jolted: shocked, made her suddenly realize.

irrevocably: finally, something that cannot be changed.

preserves: jam.

cataract: a disease of the eye that can lead to loss of sight.

bared her own soul: told Miss Roscommon about all her feelings.

grace: give a sense of grandness to.

132 *courtesy*: politeness, good manners.

strain: difficulty.

flushed: red in the face.

suppressed: kept down.

glitter: brightness, attractiveness.

emanated: gave out.

presided over: was in charge of.

shortbread: a kind of biscuit.

gesture of dismissal: movement showing that she did not think it was important.

133 *starve*: suffer or die from hunger.

frustration: feeling of being annoyed and helpless.

smugly: too pleased with themselves.

discomfited: uncomfortable, uneasy.

slop basin: bowl into which the unwanted tea at the bottom of a cup (the dregs) are poured.

134 *drawing in*: getting shorter as winter comes.

mohair: a type of fur coat.

fuss: worry about small details.

clucking round: worrying.

detained: kept.

till: a drawer where money is kept.

dreaded: greatly feared.

stifled: stopped her from developing.

preys upon: seeks to influence and control.

135 *humiliated*: made her feel ashamed.

Fortified: strengthened.

wholemeal: a type of brown bread.

intrepid: brave, fearless.

darning: mending holes, for example in socks.

Appalled: deeply shocked.

haphazardly: in a disordered way.

pandered to: tolerated, accepted without criticism.

136 *pretext*: excuse, false reason.

etching: printing.

yield: give.

Donatello: Italian sculptor (1386–1466).

stilted: stiff, formal.

woodblock engravings: printed designs.

poetry press: a company which publishes poetry books.

ethereal: light, delicate, unearthly.

137 *pierhead*: structure built out into the sea where boats can land.

gales: very strong winds.

cheval mirror: long movable mirror.

thermos flask: a type of bottle that keeps liquids hot.

lentil: a type of bean.

suffocating me: not allowing me to live freely.

all hands: all the sailors on the boat.

rent: large hole.

whimpering: making small frightened noises.

138 *vulnerable*: unprotected.

flare rocket: a type of firework that is sent up as a signal when a boat is in danger.

churned: moved violently.

139 *reassuring*: making one feel less worried.

crumpled: collapsed, in an unnatural position.

chintzy: the curtains etc. are made of a brightly-coloured cloth.

cradling: holding gently in her arms.

Questions

1. How are Miss Roscommon and Miss Bartlett contrasted?

   (a) What do we find out about the two ladies' age, appearance and character in the first four paragraphs? (p. 127)

   (b) What do we find out about Miss Roscommon's activities when she was younger? (pp. 127, 129) How did Miss Bartlett's mother treat her as a child? (pp. 128, 132, 138)

   (c) Is Miss Roscommon as confident as she appears? (pp. 127, 129)

   (d) What events show that Miss Bartlett can be hard rather than weak? (pp. 135, 137, 138)

   (e) Are the two ladies equally open about themselves with each other? (p. 131)

   (f) When they begin to live together, 'each one believed that the step was taken for the good of the other'. (p. 127) What are the two ladies' reasons for living together?

2. What is the young couple's role in the story?

   (a) Two possible reasons are given why Miss Bartlett begins to think of leaving Miss Roscommon. What are they? (p. 131)

   (b) Looking at the young couple Miss Bartlett 'felt herself to be within touching distance of some very important piece of knowledge'. (pp. 132–3) What knowledge?

   (c) Miss Bartlett wanted to say to the young couple, 'let me be on your side'. (p. 134) What would it mean to Miss Bartlett to be on their side?

   (d) Why does Miss Bartlett begin to cry when the couple leave? (p. 134)

Language Activities

Miss Bartlett's Thoughts

In 'How Soon Can I Leave?' Susan Hill gives Miss Bartlett's thoughts and the words she speaks out loud. Through both, but especially through her silent thoughts, the reader builds up a full picture of her character.

(a) In the following is Miss Bartlett saying the words out loud to herself or is she just thinking these thoughts?

   (i)   . . . she said not 'Where else would I go?' but 'I am needed here. However would she manage without me? It would be cruel to go'. (p. 130)

  (ii) Here I am, she said, . . . here I am, living my own life and making my own decisions. (p. 136)

 (iii) I have been very foolish, Miss Bartlett thought, and heard herself saying it aloud, humbly to Miss Roscommon. A very foolish, selfish woman, I do not deserve to have you as a friend. (p. 138)

(b) Account for the change in thought between, 'I have been very foolish' and, 'I will not allow myself to be treated as a pet plaything, that must be understood.' (p. 138)

Ideas for Writing

1. Imagine that Miss Roscommon is alive and well when Miss Bartlett comes to the cottage after the storm. Write out what they might say to each other in dialogue form.
Begin:
Miss Roscommon: So there you are. You know, I was very worried about you.
Miss Bartlett: Yes, I . . .

2. Write the letter that Miss Bartlett sends to Angela a year after Miss Roscommon's death. Begin 'Dear Angela, I hope you and Jack are well. I just wanted to drop you a little note to let you know what I've been up to over the last year . . .'

Katherine Mansfield

Katherine Mansfield was born in New Zealand and began her career as a writer when she came to London in her twenties. After her first, unsuccessful, marriage, she met the editor and critic, John Middleton Murry, who encouraged her in her writing, and later became her husband. The death of her younger brother in the war in 1915 made a lasting impression on her, and the memories of their childhood together in New Zealand are recreated in some of her short stories. Katherine Mansfield's stories deal with the small everyday events of life and show a particular feeling and understanding for those who are lonely or isolated. After a prolonged illness she died of tuberculosis in Fontainebleau, France at the age of 34. Her best-known collections of short stories include *Bliss* (1920), *The Garden Party* (1922) – from which this story is taken – , *The Dove's Nest* (1923) and *Something Childish* (1924).

The story

Miss Brill, a middle-aged English teacher living in France, always loves to go to the park every Sunday to watch and listen to the people around. This Sunday, however, is different . . .

Miss Brill

A LTHOUGH it was so brilliantly fine – the blue sky powdered with gold and the great spots of light like white wine splashed over the Jardins Publiques* – Miss Brill was glad that she had decided on her fur*. The air was motionless, but when you opened your mouth there was just a faint chill, like a chill from a glass of iced water before you sip*, and now and again a leaf came drifting – from nowhere, from the sky. Miss Brill put up her hand and touched her fur. Dear little thing! It was nice to feel it again. She had taken it out of its box that afternoon, shaken out the moth-powder*, given it a good brush, and rubbed the life back into the dim little eyes. 'What has been happening to me?' said the sad little eyes. Oh, how sweet it was to see them snap at her again from the red eiderdown*! . . . But the nose, which was of some black composition, wasn't at all firm. It must have had a knock, somehow. Never mind – a little dab* of black sealing-wax* when the time came – when it was absolutely necessary . . . Little rogue! Yes, she really felt like that about it. Little rogue biting its tail just by her left ear. She could have taken it off and laid it on her lap and stroked it. She felt a tingling in her hands and arms, but that came from walking, she supposed. And when she breathed, something light and sad – no, not sad, exactly – something gentle seemed to move in her bosom*.

There were a number of people out this afternoon, far more than last Sunday. And the band sounded louder and gayer. That was because the Season* had begun. For although the band played all the year round on Sundays, out of season it was never the same. It was like someone playing with only the family to listen; it didn't care how it played if there weren't any strangers present. Wasn't the conductor wearing a new coat, too? She was sure it was new. He scraped with his foot and flapped his arms like a rooster* about to crow, and the bandsmen sitting in the green rotunda* blew out their cheeks and glared at the music. Now there came a little 'flutey*' bit – very pretty! – a little chain of bright drops. She was sure it would be repeated. It was; she lifted her head and smiled.

Only two people shared her 'special' seat: a fine old man in a velvet coat, his hands clasped over a huge carved walking-stick, and a big old woman, sitting upright, with a roll of knitting on her embroidered apron. They did not speak. This was disappointing, for Miss Brill always looked forward to the conversation. She had become really quite expert, she thought, at listening as though she didn't listen, at sitting in other people's lives just for a minute while they talked round her.

She glanced, sideways, at the old couple. Perhaps they would go soon. Last Sunday, too, hadn't been as interesting as usual. An Englishman and his wife, he wearing a dreadful Panama* hat and she button boots*. And she'd gone on the whole time about how she ought to wear spectacles; she knew she needed them; but that it was no good getting any; they'd be sure to break and they'd never keep on. And he'd been so patient. He'd suggested everything – gold rims*, the kind that curved round your ears, little pads inside the bridge*. No, nothing would please her. 'They'll always be sliding down my nose!' Miss Brill had wanted to shake her.

The old people sat on the bench, still as statues. Never mind, there was always the crowd to watch. To and fro, in front of the flower-beds and the band rotunda, the couples and groups paraded, stopped to talk, to greet, to buy a handful of flowers from the old beggar who had his tray fixed to the railings*. Little children ran among them, swooping* and laughing; little boys with big white silk bows under their chins; little girls, little French dolls, dressed up in velvet and lace. And some-times a tiny staggerer* came suddenly rocking into the open from under the trees, stopped, stared, as suddenly sat down 'flop,' until its small high-stepping mother, like a young hen, rushed scolding* to its rescue. Other people sat on the benches and green chairs, but they were nearly always the same, Sun-day after Sunday, and – Miss Brill had often noticed – there was something funny about nearly all of them. They were odd, silent, nearly all old, and from the way they stared they looked as though they'd just come from dark little rooms or even – even cupboards!

Behind the rotunda the slender trees with yellow leaves down drooping, and through them just a line of sea, and beyond the blue sky with gold-veined* clouds.

Tum-tum-tum tiddle-um! tiddle-um! tum tiddley-um tum ta! blew the band.

Two young girls in red came by and two young soldiers in blue met them, and they laughed and paired and went off arm in arm. Two peasant women with funny straw hats passed, gravely*, leading beautiful smoke-coloured donkeys. A cold, pale nun hurried by. A beautiful woman came along and dropped her bunch of violets, and a little boy ran after to hand them to her, and she took them and threw them away as if they'd been poisoned. Dear me! Miss Brill didn't know whether to admire that or not! And now an ermine toque* and a gentleman in grey met just in front of her. He was tall, stiff, dignified, and she was wearing the ermine toque she'd bought when her hair was yellow. Now everything, her hair, her face, even her eyes, was the same colour as the shabby* ermine, and her hand, in its cleaned glove, lifted to dab* her lips, was a tiny yellowish paw*. Oh, she was so pleased to see him – delighted! She rather thought they were going to meet that afternoon. She described where she'd been – everywhere, here, there, along by the sea. The day was so charming – didn't he agree? And wouldn't he, perhaps? . . . But he shook his head, lighted a cigarette, slowly breathed a great deep puff into her face and, even while she was still talking and laughing, flicked the match away and walked on. The ermine toque was alone; she smiled more brightly than ever. But even the band seemed to know what she was feeling and played more softly, played tenderly, and the drum beat 'The Brute*! The Brute!' over and over. What would she do? What was going to happen now? But as Miss Brill wondered, the ermine toque turned, raised her hand as though she'd seen someone else, much nicer, just over there, and pattered away*. And the band changed again and played more quickly, more gaily than ever, and the old couple on Miss Brill's seat got up and marched away, and such a funny old man with long whiskers hobbled* along in time to the music and was nearly knocked over by four girls walking abreast*.

Oh, how fascinating it was! How she enjoyed it! How she loved sitting here, watching it all! It was like a play. It was exactly like a play. Who could believe the sky at the back wasn't painted? But it wasn't till a little brown dog trotted on* solemnly and then slowly trotted off, like a little 'theatre' dog, a little dog that had been drugged*, that Miss Brill discovered what it was that made it so exciting. They were all on the stage. They weren't only the audience, not only looking on; they were acting. Even she had a part and came every Sunday. No doubt somebody would have noticed if she hadn't been there; she was part of the performance, after all. How strange she'd never thought of it like that before! And yet it explained why she made such a point of starting from home at just the same time each week – so as not to be late for the performance – and it also explained why she had quite a queer*, shy feeling at telling her English pupils how she spent her Sunday afternoons. No wonder! Miss Brill nearly laughed out loud. She was on the stage. She thought of the old invalid gentleman to whom she read the newspaper four afternoons a week while he slept in the garden. She had got quite used to the frail* head on the cotton pillow, the hollowed eyes, the open mouth and the high pinched* nose. If he'd been dead she mightn't have noticed for weeks; she wouldn't have minded. But suddenly he knew he was having the paper read to him by an actress! 'An actress!' The old head lifted; two points of light quivered* in the old eyes. 'An actress – are ye?' And Miss Brill smoothed the newspaper as though it were the manuscript of her part and said gently: 'Yes, I have been an actress for a long time.'

The band had been having a rest. Now they started again. And what they played was warm, sunny, yet there was just a faint chill – a something, what was it? – not sadness – no, not sadness – a something that made you want to sing. The tune lifted, lifted, the light shone; and it seemed to Miss Brill that in another moment all of them, all the whole company, would begin singing. The young ones, the laughing ones who were moving together, they would begin, and the men's voices, very resolute* and brave, would join them. And then she too, she too, and the others on the benches – they would come in with a kind of accompaniment* – something low, that scarcely rose or fell, something so beautiful – moving. . . . And Miss Brill's eyes filled with tears and she looked smiling at all the other members of the company. Yes, we understand, we understand, she thought – though what they understood she didn't know.

Just at that moment a boy and a girl came and sat down where the old couple had been. They were beautifully dressed; they were in love. The hero and heroine, of course, just arrived from his father's yacht*. And still soundlessly singing, still with that trembling smile, Miss Brill prepared to listen.

'No, not now,' said the girl. 'Not here, I can't.'

'But why? Because of that stupid old thing at the end there?' asked the boy. 'Why does she come here at all – who wants her? Why doesn't she keep her silly old mug* at home?'

'It's her fu-fur which is so funny,' giggled the girl. 'It's exactly like a fried whiting*.'

'Ah, be off with you*!' said the boy in an angry whisper. Then: 'Tell me, ma petite chère* –'

'No, not here,' said the girl. 'Not *yet*.'

On her way home she usually bought a slice of honey-cake at the baker's. It was her Sunday treat. Sometimes there was an almond* in her slice, sometimes not. It made a great difference. If there was an almond it was like carrying home a tiny present – a surprise – something that might very well not have been there. She hurried on the almond Sundays and struck the match for the kettle in quite a dashing* way.

But to-day she passed the baker's by, climbed the stairs, went into the little dark room – her room like a cupboard – and sat down on the red eiderdown. She sat there for a long time. The box that the fur came out of was on the bed. She unclasped the necklet* quickly; quickly, without looking, laid it inside. But when she put the lid on she thought she heard something crying.

Glossary

The meanings given below are those which the words and phrases have as they occur in the story.

Page

147   *Jardins Publiques (French)*: public gardens.

fur: a fox fur worn around a woman's neck.

sip: take a little drink.

moth-powder: powder that kills moths (an insect that eats holes in cloth, fur etc.)

eiderdown: a thick bed covering.

little dab: small amount.

sealing-wax: substance that melts and hardens quickly, at one time used to seal (close) envelopes.

bosom: breast, the centre of one's feelings.

Season: period of the year when there are fashionable social events.

rooster: male chicken.

rotunda: round building with a bowl-shaped roof, place where a band plays in a public park.

flutey: light sounds made by the wind instruments of the band (e.g. flutes).

148   *Panama*: a type of straw hat.

button boots: old-fashioned boots done up by buttons.

rims: the metal edges of spectacles.

bridge: part of the spectacles that goes over the nose.

railings: metal fence.

swooping: rushing up suddenly.

staggerer: a baby who cannot walk very well.

scolding: speaking in an angry, complaining way.

149   *gold-veined*: clouds with gold colour on their edges.

gravely: seriously.

ermine toque: a woman's hat made of white fur.

shabby: much worn, old-looking.

dab: touch lightly.

paw: like an animal's foot.

Brute: cruel, insensitive man.

pattered away: ran with short quick steps.

150 *hobbled*: moved with difficulty.
  abreast: side by side.
  trotted on: came quickly with short steps.
  drugged: given a drug so that it would perform on stage without getting too nervous.
  queer: strange.
  frail: weak.
  pinched: thin.
  quivered: moved slightly.
151 *resolute*: strong, determined.
  accompaniment: music played to support the singing.
  yacht: large boat owned by a rich person for pleasure purposes.
  mug (sl.): face.
  whiting: a kind of fish.
  be off with you (coll.): go away.
  ma petite chère (French): my little dear.
  almond: a kind of nut.
  dashing: lively, stylish.
  necklet: the fox fur.

Questions

1. What is the significance of the events that take place in the park?

   (a) Why is Miss Brill disappointed with the old couple who sit on her seat and the English couple she listened to the previous Sunday? (p. 148) What sort of things would she prefer to hear and why?

   (b) Why do you think the beautiful woman threw her bunch of violets away? (p. 149)

   (c) Why do you think the gentleman in grey is so rude to the lady in the ermine toque? (p. 149)

   (d) In what ways are the ermine and Miss Brill's fur similar? In what way is Miss Brill later treated similarly to the lady with the ermine? (pp. 147, 149, 151)

2. How are young and old people contrasted in the story?
   (a) Describe the crowd the old people sitting on the bench with Miss Brill can see in front of them? (p. 148)
   (b) Why do you think that most of the people on the benches every Sunday are old and silent? What does it mean when Miss Brill says that they look as though they have come from cupboards? (pp. 148–50)
   (c) How does Miss Brill normally spend her afternoons during the week? (p. 150)
   (d) Why do the young couple on Miss Brill's bench want her to go? What do they not like about her? (p. 151)

3. How is the idea of illusions important in the story?

   (a) Why does Miss Brill talk to her fur as though it were alive? (p. 147)
   (b) Why is Miss Brill excited about the idea of being an 'actress' rather than a member of an 'audience' in the park? (p. 150)
   (c) Why does Miss Brill call the young couple a 'hero and heroine . . . just arrived from his father's yacht'? (p. 151)
   (d) What do you understand by the last sentence? (p. 151)

Language Activities

Miss Brill's Thoughts

(a) The whole of Katherine Mansfield's story is a sensitive presentation of Miss Brill's thoughts and feelings.
   Look at the passage from 'What has been happening to me?' to 'biting its tail just by her left ear' in the first paragraph. (p. 147)

   (i) Who says, 'What has been happening to me?'
   (ii) Why are there three dots before 'But the nose . . .'?
   (iii) What does 'when it was absolutely necessary' mean here?
   (iv) 'Little rogue!' Who is this spoken to?
   (v) What is the difference between: 'She really felt like that

about it': and, 'Yes, she really felt like that about it'?

(b) In the story the band and the music it plays reflect and parallel Miss Brill's changing thoughts and attitudes.

   (i) 'And the band sounded louder and gayer.' (p. 147) How is Miss Brill feeling at this point?

   (ii) 'But even the band seemed to know what she was feeling and played more softly, played tenderly, and the drum beat "The Brute! The Brute!" over and over.' (p. 149)
   What has just happened here? How do you think Miss Brill feels about this event?

   (iii) 'The tune lifted, lifted, the light shone: and it seemed to Miss Brill that in another moment all of them, all the whole company, would begin singing.' (p. 150) Why is Miss Brill so happy that 'the whole company' is singing together?

Ideas for Writing

1. Write out what Miss Brill usually tells her pupils about her Sunday afternoons. Begin 'I'd like to tell you all what I do on my Sunday afternoons . . .'

2. Write two fairly short letters: one written by Miss Brill to a friend in England describing her visit to the park on the previous Sunday: and the other to the same friend on the evening she came back home after being rudely treated by the young couple.

* * * * * *

1. Which of these two stories do you prefer? What are some of the reasons for your choice?

2. What do you imagine Miss Bartlett's and Miss Brill's lives will be like in the future?